Therapists' Acclaim for
Handwriting for Heroes

"I've used *Handwriting for Heroes* with all of my patients, some lost hand function from amputation, brachial plexus injuries, stroke, or extensive soft tissue trauma to the dominant hand. All of my patients benefited and enjoyed the workbook and how it helped them return to handwriting tasks."

—Stephanie E. Daugherty, MS, OTR/L, CHT, US Army Lt. Col. (ret.)

"*Handwriting for Heroes* is extremely practical and functional! It is an ESSENTIAL tool in hand dominance retraining for the upper limb amputee."

—Oren S. Ganz, MOT, OTR/L

"*Handwriting for Heroes* is more than a workbook! It's an investment into the future performance of my patients who need to return to occupations that demand handwriting. My patients enjoy the challenge and the success of the program!"

—Kristi A. Say, OTR/L

"*Handwriting for Heroes* is truly an amazing skill building intervention that truly works! I had the opportunity to participate in during its development as a healthy research subject, and through the daily exercises and practice sessions I developed the ability to write competently with my left hand; a skill that I am still able to exercise, demonstrating that it a sustainable learned skill and behavior. As someone trained in the science of research, *Handwriting for Heroes* is remarkable because it represents an experimental intervention that not only worked but has profound utility in the realm of rehabilitation sciences."

-Alex F. Howard, MPH, ATC

Patient Experiences

"After losing my dominant (right) hand while covering a story in Iraq in 2003, I used this handwriting manual to learn how to write with my left hand. It helped me to take notes again, a valuable contribution to my recovery."

—Michael Weisskopf, *Time Magazine* Reporter

"This program has really helped with my confidence in my handwriting. Now I write a lot better and faster."

—Christian Ivory, Senior Airman, USAF

"After injuring my hand while serving in Afghanistan, I used *Handwriting for Heroes* to learn how to write again using my non-dominant hand. The workbook allowed me an opportunity to practice writing each day. Over the 6 weeks program, I mastered the skills necessary to write legibly again."

—SSG Keaton Nielson, USAR

After injuring my right hand in Afghanistan I needed to learn how to write again with my left hand. Handwriting for Heroes taught me how in 6 weeks. By using the workbook daily I was able to master what I thought was going to be a near impossible task.

Then when I was able to gain use of my right hand again, I used the same principles to re-learn how to write again with my hand. The Hand writing for Heroes taught me how to write twice.

—SSG Keaton Nielson, US Army Reserve

Reviewers' Acclaim

"*Handwriting for Heroes* is an essential tool for the recovery of both body and spirit. Occupational Therapists, Prosthetics and Orthotics professionals, and those recovering from amputation, severe physical injury, or stroke can all benefit from the information and exercises contained in this book. Authors Kathleen E. Yancosek and Kristin Gulick deliver tried and true methods from week one through week six on accomplishing this goal and even include a certificate of completion at the conclusion."

Vicki Landes, *ReviewTheBook.com*

"The authors have written a very exceptional workbook to help those individuals with dominant-hand problems regain their writing skills. I believe as the authors do, it is important that individuals utilizing this workbook experience positive outcomes. Each chapter is built off the previous one. If a person doesn't understand something, or needs additional help, it is suggested that they go to the website and speak to a therapist. I found the exercises and lessons interesting, easy to understand and use. There are many people who cannot afford therapy for extended periods of time or are embarrassed about the limited use of their dominant hand. This excellent workbook, *Handwriting for Heroes*, by Yancosek and Gulick, is for them."

Carol Hoyer, PhD, for *Reader Views*

"This workbook is designed to help those individuals with dominant-hand problems or injuries regain their writing skills and self respect. The authors did a wonderful job with this workbook. If you have a non-dominant-hand injury or just want to learn to write with you opposite hand, look no further. I recommend this book to anyone wishing to learn how to write with their non-dominant hand. "

Randy A. Lakin, for *Rebeccas Reads*

"Developed by two experienced Occupational and Hand Therapists to help you learn to write with your non-dominant hand, *Handwriting for Heroes* is an encouraging but no-nonsense program for those who are serious about switching dominant sides. Daily and weekly practice assignments, tips for assuring success, and plenty of encouraging words are offered in a framework of adult interests and sensibilities – no more first-grade writing tablets and kid-level practice sentences! The workbook is well-organized, clear, and comprehensive. The authors even invite the user to visit their website to ask questions or report on their progress."

Bonnie Pike, Director www.StepUp-SpeakOut.org (a lymphedema support group)

"*Handwriting for Heroes* is a six week program to teach you how to write with your non-dominant hand. I am normally right-handed and enjoyed each of the exercises while trying out my left hand. I felt like I was in kindergarten when doing the pages because when I write with my right hand it is so easy, but when I write with my left hand it was such a challenge. I love the challenge and took it on and have to admit that I did it faster than I had expected. I also think that it used my brain in a form that I was not previously aware I had. If someone has an injury to their hand, they can use this book to learn how to write again and this is the first book for adult learners published: what a great idea! I think all doctors' offices, chiropractors, and any-one who helps others with healing from injuries would benefit from this book. I am very im-pressed with Kathleen Yancosek and her team's idea to publish this one-of-a-kind book on handwriting."

Jackie Paulsen Reviews

Handwriting for HEROES

Third Edition

Learn To Write With Your Non-dominant Hand in Six Weeks

Kathleen E. Yancosek, PhD, OTR/L, CHT
Kristin Gulick, OTR/L, CHT
Amanda Sammons, DSc, OTR/L

LOVING HEALING PRESS

Published by:
Loving Healing Press, Inc.
5145 Pontiac Trail
Ann Arbor, MI 48105-9627

Web site: www.LHPress.com
Email: info@LHPress.com
Tollfree: 888-761-6268
Fax: 734-663-6861

Distributed by:
New Leaf Distributing
www.newleaf-dist.com

"Redefining what is possible for healing mind and spirit"
Since 2003

Printed in the United States of America.

CONTENTS

Can I scan or copy pages out of Handwriting For Heroes?

We hesitated to say "no" because we want you and your patients to use the workbook, but we did copyright the material and honestly believe that each patient *should* own and complete his or her own workbook. This way the intervention is personalized and they are responsible for completing each day's lesson AND you can check it and praise their progress and commitment to recovery.

Copyright violation is a Federal crime (Title 18, U.S.C. 2319).

If you are feel the need for a few sample pages to get a person interested in trying the program, please feel free to download the Extra Credit pages that are available (and free) on the *Handwriting for Heroes* webpage:

www.handwritingforheroes.com/extra-credit/

PREFACE

For the past 20 years, I have been a team player with many individuals, many heroes, both civilian and military, whose upper-limb limitations or amputations led them to tackle the challenge of changing dominance. For a small number, it came relatively easily, for the majority the challenge was great. For all, success was dependent on determination.

Like Katie, I knew I could strengthen my therapeutic role by undergoing the process of training my non-dominant left hand to write. My first attempt was incredibly frustrating. Later, I concluded the primary problem was my lack of commitment to the challenge. I must admit I tried to cram my initial attempts into a busy schedule and thought maybe, just maybe, being a hand therapist would make it come easily. I can tell you that being a therapist gives me no special skills in this arena. My first practice session disregarded all of my "tips". I was standing at the kitchen counter with inadequate light, preoccupied waiting for the veterinarian to call about a sick foal. No matter how familiar I was with multitasking, I certainly set myself up for failure! Within 10 minutes my teeth were clenched and my hand was cramping. I quit.

A few days later, I set aside focused time. 30 minutes of quiet time. I put on some calming music, sat in a good chair at an appropriate height table with good light and started in. Ahh... much better! Until human endeavor is entirely subsumed by technology, handwriting remains a life skill and craft. Personally, I hope that handwriting does not go the way of the 8-track tape. There is nothing like the thrill of receiving a handwritten letter. I often find the handwritten sticky note on the word-processed printout is the rare message I receive with a touch of humanity. Emails almost never convey the intensity and sincerity of handwritten words. So, I believe the commitment required to learn this life skill is worth it!

Please use my initial failure to your advantage. Set yourself up for success. We truly hope that working with this manual will ease the transition to change dominance. Please email us, (I would say write us, but email is quicker), if we can help in any way.

DEDICATION

This manual is dedicated to the military heroes I have been honored to serve as the leader of the occupational therapy amputee section at Walter Reed Army Medical Center in Washington D.C. I thank them for their courage to endure the pain and loss associated with amputation and to push forward to independence. The many amputees who lost their dominant hand and had to retrain their remaining limb in the craft and skill of handwriting inspired this workbook. They allowed me to gratefully learn along side them as they mastered handwriting again. To experience what it was like for them, I worked to be able to write with my non-dominant left hand. "Work" is the key word! It was not easy. Once a few were successful at the dominance transfer, I was compelled to capture what they did and make it available to others so they can attain mastery too.

Katie Yancosek

ACKNOWLEDGEMENTS

I want to acknowledge and thank the therapists with whom I worked at Walter Reed: Oren Ganz, Lisa Smurr, Harvey Naranjo, Ibrahim Kabbah, Kristi Say, Michelle Hunter, and Avery Pegeus. They have all contributed to the development and process of creating this manual, as well as worked with many patients during the process of hand dominance transfer.

Thank you to Erin Spears for his unique contribution of the artwork in this manual. He worked creatively to make the art challenging and suitable to an adult population.

Thank you to Jenny Tanaka for her administrative support in assembling the manual. Her eye for detail was irreplaceable.

Katie & Kristin

INTRODUCTION

Recruiting your Dendrites

As you begin the difficult task of transferring dominance, give yourself permission to acknowledge the following statements:

- ## This will take a big commitment of my time and energy.

- ## I will be clumsy at controlling the pencil.

- ## My handwriting will NOT be neat.

Return to these statements as often as necessary to recommit to this process. Also, rely on your Occupational Therapist, (OT), to provide direction, should you be struggling in a specific task. The OT is the expert therapist trained in hand function, including the fine motor control you will need to successfully transfer your hand skill. If you do not have an OT, you have email access to one at www.handwritingforheroes.com

A final note of caution: this is a six week process. You should work each day for six weeks, until you have mastered the basic skills of cursive writing.

Handwriting, like all tasks, improves with daily repetition. Repetition is built into this program in order to help your brain and hand coordinate the smooth, quick motions needed for legible cursive writing. The program's format is designed to give you visual feedback of your daily progress. There are 13 exercises for each day, and you will always need to devote a week's worth of work for each exercise. The reward will be to see your own daily improvements.

Strive to go beyond yesterday's level. Don't expect perfection. Allow yourself room for improvement. This takes a long-term mental and emotional, as well as physical commitment!

INTRODUCTION TO THE 3ʳᴰ EDITION

In addition to the 'Daily Dozen' exercises, the 3ʳᵈ edition of *Handwriting for Heroes* includes a special 'Baker's Dozen' created by Dr. Amanda Sammons, an Army occupational therapist. This newly developed section helps you cultivate a positive attitude and "MIGHTY Mindset" throughout your course of recovery and handwriting skill development. Edward George Bulwer Lytton said, "The pen is mightier than the sword". Writing is a very powerful tool, and gains more strength when coupled with a positive attitude to influence the thoughts behind your writing. The 'Baker's Dozen' offers positive psychology exercises to promote optimism and resiliency in your daily life. One of the primary aims of positive psychology is to help people to discover, explore, and improve on their personal strengths. This can be done through a variety of deliberate exercises to train your brain to attend more to your positive experiences and focus less on the negative ones. Throughout this program you will complete a positive psychology exercise each day.

The word **MIGHTY** is used as a mnemonic to help you remember each of the positive psychology exercises that you will learn during your journey to change hand dominance.

M: Mindfulness

I: Improve your signature strengths

G: Gratitude

H: Happiness advantage

T: Three good things

Y: You at your best

Each week focuses on a different aspect of positive psychology. Apply each to your day-to-day life regardless of where you are in the process of changing your hand dominance. In fact, these exercises should become part of your daily routine for you to continually cultivate a positive attitude and mighty mindset.

~ ~ ~

Cursive writing is easier than printing from motor and perceptual standpoints. Learning cursive writing also diminishes the challenge of having even spaces between printed letters. However, many have requested that the 3ʳᵈ edition include instructions and visual demonstrations on PRINT writing. We have answered your request. To keep the workbook a reasonable length, we have placed *both* a print and cursive example at the top of each exercise page. Please feel free to do both *or* select the type/style of writing you wish to master and stick to it. Where space was limited, we placed the print example in parenthesis.

We welcome your feedback at **www.handwritingforheroes.com** - Kristin, Katie, and Amanda

THERAPIST GUIDE

First and foremost, *YOU* must become adept at handwriting with your non-dominant hand. Complete this manual and work to transfer your own dominance. In this way, you'll know the arduous process of transferring dominance, as well as you have confidence in this program. Please send us feedback of your experience. We feel an obligation to our profession, as well as a duty to provide evidence based practice and create the best interventions to our patients. Please take this journey seriously because you'll be giving your patients a level of independence and a sense of autonomy that is well worth the effort. It is important to merge the knowledge that we have from neurological, biological, psychological, developmental, and kinesiological sources. Recall the principle of plasticity that drives so much of our work in neurorehabilitation and pediatric rehabilitation.

Look for the lightbulb symbol in the manual for *Therapists' Training Tips*. Please consult us on the website as needed. www.handwritingforheroes.com

The book is formatted to maximize the two hallmarks of motor learning: repetition and feedback. The format is such that the patient will receive daily visual feedback of his/her work (thereby noticing improvement) and will repeat a series of skill-building, fine-motor exercises. There are homework exercises each day. These are not extra, suggested activities. They are an integral part of the program and need to be completed in order to maximize the learning process.

CHANGE
By Kari Brown

Everything changes; nothing stays the same
Just when you think you're fine
Change comes along with a spiteful smile
He switches everything around
With mischievous glee
Change watches you struggle to make right
What he just made wrong
And just when you finally succeed
He comes along again and undoes all that you just did
Change jumps at every chance he gets
To mess something up in life
Change loves to pull a prank
And laughs when it works perfectly
Just like he had planned it
You're up to bat in the dangerous game of Living
Change is pitching everything
He can strike you out
Or tease you with a home run
Change has everything under control
Even or maybe especially when you think you do

OVERVIEW

Each session involves completion of a set of exercises, a "Baker's dozen". On each of the seven pages, one for each day of the week, you will complete one line per day. As you progress through the week, you will be able to look back on each page to see how your handwriting changes with practice. The 13 exercises designed to build the hand's fine motor control and wrist stabilization to excel at hand writing with the non-dominant hand. Please heed the prompt to take a rest and stretch break in the middle of each session!

1. Warm ups
2. Train in the rain
3. Range control
4. Stretches
5. Spit shine
6. Speed drills
7. Boot lacing
8. In cadence
9. Carbon copy
10. Steady at the ready
11. Endurance training
12. Esprit de corps
13. MIGHTY Mindfulness exercise

Training the non-dominant hand to write is an arduous task but, nonetheless, a necessary one when the dominant hand has permanent, or partial, loss of function.

Regardless of transferring left to right or right to left, you will be completing the same series of exercises. Each session consists of a bonus page and a required homework assignment.

Tips for the therapist are incorporated in each week's lesson. If you are the patient and working this program without the assistance of a therapist and you have difficulties or questions, please contact an occupational therapist through the website www.handwritingforheroes.com

Self-Perception Questionnaire on Handwriting Ability Pre-Test

Instructions: Using a 0 - 10 Scale, please answer the following questions about your handwriting ability.

1. How does your handwriting ability *today* compare to your handwriting ability *before* your limb injury in terms of __readability__?
Readability means that someone who doesn't know you can read what you wrote.

0	1	2	3	4	5	6	7	8	9	10
not at all alike										exactly alike

2. How does your handwriting ability *today* compare to your handwriting ability *before* your limb injury in terms of __speed__?
Speed means the pace at which you are writing.

0	1	2	3	4	5	6	7	8	9	10
not at all alike										exactly alike

3. How does your handwriting ability *today* compare to your handwriting *before* your limb injury in terms of __appearance__.
Appearance means the shape, size, slant, and style of your writing.

0	1	2	3	4	5	6	7	8	9	10
not at all alike										exactly alike

4. How __confident__ are you in your writing ability?
Confidence means that you are sure of your ability to write.

0	1	2	3	4	5	6	7	8	9	10
not confident at all										exactly alike

5. How __important__ is learning to write again?
Important means that you value spending your time learning to write again.

0	1	2	3	4	5	6	7	8	9	10
not confident at all										exactly alike

Handwriting for Heroes

Week One

It is important to set realistic goals for myself.
Be specific and think about improving your speed,
legibility, endurance, commitment, and motivation.
This week my handwriting goal is:

_____

_____

_____

_____

Exercise 1: Warm-ups

Make X's in the boxes as demonstrated in the first box in each row.

Day 1:

Day 2:

Day 3:

Day 4:

Day 5:

Day 6:

Day 7:

Exercise 2: Train in the rain

Write two lines of this example each day:

ccccccccccccccccccccccccccccccccccccccccccccc

ccccccccccccccccccccccccccccccccccccccccccccc

Day 1:

_____

_____

Day 2:

_____

_____

Day 3:

_____

_____

Day 4:

_____

_____

Day 5:

_____

_____

Day 6:

_____

_____

Day 7:

_____

_____

1-3

Exercise 3: Range control

This exercise is about stretching and growing. Trace the following curvy line .

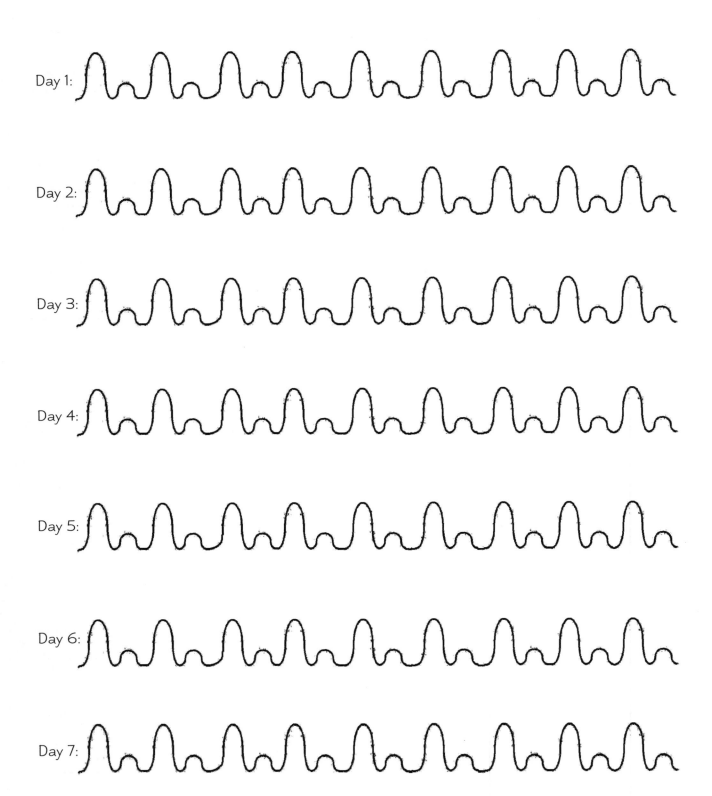

Day 1:

Day 2:

Day 3:

Day 4:

Day 5:

Day 6:

Day 7:

Exercise 4: Stretches

Write the following line of continuous letters twice. Be consistent with your slant. Do not lift your pen or pencil until you need to start the second line.

ccccccc   qqqqqqq   ddddddd   gggggg   oooooo

ccccccc   qqqqqqqq   ddddddd   gggggg   oooooo

Day 1:

_____

_____

Day 2:

_____

_____

Day 3:

_____

_____

Day 4:

_____

_____

Day 5:

_____

_____

Day 6:

_____

_____

Day 7:

_____

Exercise 5: Spit shine

Repetition and attention to details put the polishing touches on anything. In the Military, that's what makes a good spit shine. In the following exercises, copy the following two lines:

gogogogogogogogogogogogogogo (go go go go go)

Cacacacacacacacacacacacaca (caca caca caca)

Day 1: _____

_____

Day 2: _____

_____

Day 3: _____

_____

Day 4: _____

_____

Day 5: _____

_____

Day 6: _____

_____

Day 7: _____

_____

Exercise 6: Speed drills

Write the series of letters seven times on each day's lines. Move quickly. Speed is more important than neatness in this exercise.

caodgq caodgq caodgq caodgq caodgq caodgq
caodgq caodgq caodgq caodgq caodgq caodgq

Day 1:

Day 2:

Day 3:

Day 4:

Day 5:

Day 6:

Day 7:

Exercise 7: Boot lacing

These two words include two frequently written letters that require you to lift your pen from the paper. As you resume writing, remember to maintain your slant. Copy these two lines:

exit exit exit exit exit exit exit exit exit (exit)

exceptional exceptional exceptional (exceptional)

Day 1: _____

_____

Day 2: _____

_____

Day 3: _____

_____

Day 4: _____

_____

Day 5: _____

_____

Day 6: _____

_____

Day 7: _____

_____

Exercise 8: In cadence

Cursive Learners: Trace inside the outlined words. Please use a pencil for this exercise.
Print learners: Below the cursive example, write the sentence,

"I take one day at a time."

Day 1: *I take one day at a time!*

Day 2: *I take one day at a time!*

Day 3: *I take one day at a time!*

Day 4: *I take one day at a time!*

Day 5: *I take one day at a time!*

Day 6: *I take one day at a time!*

Day 7: *I take one day at a time!*

Exercise 9: Carbon copy

The following sentence contains every letter of the alphabet....really! You won't even know you've written the alphabet. It's the medicine-in-the-applesauce method of writing your ABCs. Write the sentence twice. How's your slant, by the way?

The quick brown fox jumps over the lazy dog.

The quick brown fox jumps over the lazy dog.

Day 1: _____

_____

Day 2: _____

_____

Day 3: _____

_____

Day 4: _____

_____

Day 5: _____

_____

Day 6: _____

_____

Day 7: _____

_____

Exercise 10: Steady at the Ready

Cursive Learners: you will combine "straight line" and "loop" letters. When you transition between line and loop, please pay careful attention to keeping your proper slant. Copy the following sentence once each day.

I must overlook a lot of mistakes in my writing early on.

I must overlook a lot of mistakes in my writing early on.

Day 1: _____

_____

Day 2: _____

_____

Day 3: _____

_____

Day 4: _____

_____

Day 5: _____

_____

Day 6: _____

_____

Day 7: _____

_____

Exercise 11: Endurance training   NOW, neatness counts! . Copy this sentence:

When I focus my energy and attention on learning to write these words, I can succeed.

When I focus my energy and attention on learning to write these words, I can succeed.

Day 1: _____

_____

Day 2: _____

_____

Day 3: _____

_____

Day 4: _____

_____

Day 5: _____

_____

Day 6: _____

_____

Day 7: _____

_____

Exercise 12: Esprit de corps

Copy these two sentences on each of the day's two lines:

I am working toward improving my writing skills and that takes time.

I am working toward improving my writing skills and that takes time.

*Review today's work and place a STAR next to today's best writing.

Day 1:

_____

_____

Day 2:

_____

_____

Day 3:

_____

_____

Day 4:

_____

_____

Day 5:

_____

_____

Day 6:

_____

_____

Day 7:

_____

Exercise 13: Mighty Mindset Exercise: <u>M</u>indfulness

The concept of mindfulness is used to focus our awareness on the present moment that we are experiencing. Mindfulness can be used as a resource to help you better understand and accept your emotions in a healthy way. There are three primary concepts to being mindful: paying attention on purpose, being in the present moment, and accepting all thoughts and emotions non-judgmentally.

When we go through the motions of our daily routine we often don't attend to each experience that we are having. For example, drinking your morning coffee. When not being mindful you might just be aware of the hot temperature of your drink, the smell of coffee grounds, and the routine taste of your morning pick-me-up.

The difference when being mindful is to take the opportunity to truly be in present and experience the moment of taking your first sip of coffee. This means being aware of all five of your senses: taste, touch, sight, smell, and sound.
   Before even picking up your coffee cup examining the color, size, and shape of the glass
   Taking a deep inhale through your nose and attending to the robust aromas the coffee produces
   Feeling the warmth of the cup against the palms of your hands
   Seeing the streaks of steam billowing off the top of the light brown liquid and dissipating into the air
   Feeling the warmth of the cup against your lip before you even take your first sip

See the difference!

Mindfulness is something that you can practice with ANY of your daily activities. It may take you ten minutes to take the first sip of coffee, but the difference in your mindset when you get there can make all the difference.

Exercise 13: Mighty Mindset Exercise: <u>M</u>indfulness

Day 1: Two Mindful Bites

It would be very challenging to try to be mindful for your entire meal. Instead, try mindful eating for the first two bites of any meal or snack that you eat.
Make sure to pay attention to the sensory experiences of those two bites (visual appearance of food, textures you both see and feel, sensations of food in your mouth, the sounds you hear while chewing, etc.).

Day 2: The Game of Fives

Look around the room and notice five things that your can see. Really look at each item and experience what you are seeing and thinking.
This time scan the room for five things you can hear.
Now really get into the moment and identify five things that you can smell.

Day 3: Feel each breath

Take a few minutes to yourself to experience the sensations that accompany each breath that you take.
Feel the air coming in and out of your body with each breath. Take note of where you can physically feel your body expanding as the air enters your lungs. Can you hear yourself inhaling and exhaling?

Day 4: Feel the weight of your clothes

We wear clothing and don't actually feel each article of clothing that we have on. After we are finished getting dressed our body gets used to the sensation of the clothing and we forget about it. Take time to experience one article of clothing. Become aware how materials feels against your skin. Notice the weight of the cloth against your body.

Days 5: Write with feelings

Think about writing: how does the paper feel against the side of your hand, how does the pen feel in your fingers. When you place pressure through the pen, what do your fingers feel as you form each letter. Slow down and enjoy being able to form each distinct curve of each letter. Writing is quite a complex task. Enjoy your ability to engage in such a complex activity.

Days 6, and 7: Your choice of a mindfulness exercise. Repeat one of the techniques you practiced this week; or select any activity that is part of your routine and experience it with mindful awareness!

THERAPISTS' TIPS

WHAT SHOULD YOU USE TO LEARN TO WRITE WITH?

We suggest beginning with a #3 pencil, as it is not as likely to smudge if your hand rubs across the words. Using a pencil provides some proprioceptive feedback to your joints. This reinforces the learning process. The pencil has medium drag, which is a good place to begin. What we mean by drag is that the lead has some resistance across the page. A ballpoint pen would have less and a crayon or felt tip marker would have more. If you feel that you are working too hard you may want to try a ballpoint pen. If you feel that you are sliding or lack control, you may want to try a felt tip marker.

DO SPECIAL GRIPS HELP?

A larger diameter grip is often easier to hold than the typical pencil or pen. It decreases the amount of force required to grip the writing device. This is especially true if you have any arthritis at the joint at the base of your thumb. The joint at the base of the thumb is placed in a better position with a larger grip. This principle extends to any tool you may use, i.e. hammer, and crowbar, even a golf club.

If you simply want to enlarge the diameter of your writing tool you can purchase pens with enlarged grips. The enlarged area is also often non-slip to help you decrease the amount of pressure that you need to hold the pen. If you are using a pencil you could start by wrapping some Coban around the area that you place your thumb and fingers. This will increase the diameter, as well as provide a non-slip area. If this is helpful you can purchase slip on sleeves, often made from a type of foam from office supply stores or NorthCoast Medical.

There are also grips that help to correctly position your fingers on the writing tool. The one pictured below is available at www.DrawYourWorld.com, www.AllTheWriteNews.com, or Google for "pencil grips." There is a Jumbo Grip that is good for someone with arthritis. There are smaller grips called Mini Grips for people with smaller hands. The grips can be used for right or left-handed writers. It may take some trial and error to find what helps you the most.

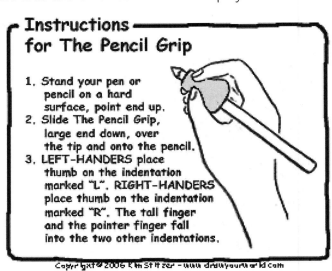

Instructions for The Pencil Grip

1. Stand your pen or pencil on a hard surface, point end up.
2. Slide The Pencil Grip, large end down, over the tip and onto the pencil.
3. LEFT-HANDERS place thumb on the indentation marked "L". RIGHT-HANDERS place thumb on the indentation marked "R". The tall finger and the pointer finger fall into the two other indentations.

Copyright © 2006 Kim Stitzer - www.drawyourworld.com

1-16

Week One: Homework for Heroes

Day 1: While you're sitting and watching television, practice flipping a pen from end to end in your hand. If that's too easy, get a pen with a cap on it and put it on and take it off at each end (repeatedly) without dropping the pen or the cap.

Day 2: Place coins or marbles or buttons in Silly Putty or Theraputty and work your fingers to pull the objects out. This builds strength and dexterity in your hand.

Day 3: Complete the coloring page following these instructions.

Day 4: Practice your signature by writing it as many times as you can. Use the signature page provided in this week's homework section. Write it in the margins and in many directions. You will feel so good about yourself once you have mastered a nice signature again. You will be proud to use your credit card and sign your name to "seal the deal" of the purchase! ☺

Day 5: Roll coins in coin wrappers. This is an excellent fine motor coordination task and one that works on the control of your thumb, index and middle fingers.

Day 6: Practice printing a few things that you will likely always print, like your email address and your home address. Use the page provided in the homework section for this week.

Day 7: Complete the dot to dot activity following these instructions.

~ ~ ~

Well you did it! You completed the first week—the toughest week—of the handwriting program. You are on your way to becoming a "Handwriting Hero".

You'll continue with the baker's dozen each week, and when you're done with the six weeks of "Basic Training" you'll be ready for all basic, cursive and/or printing writing tasks.

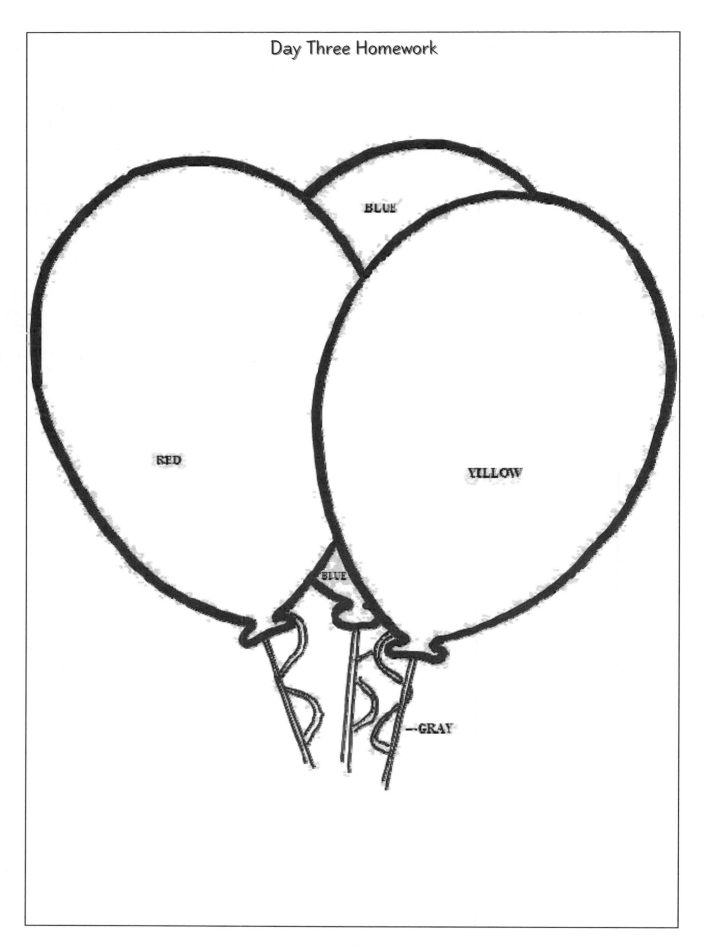

Day Four Homework

Practice your signature by writing it as many times as you can. Come on, Print Learners, you have to do some cursive writing for *THIS* activity. You want to have a signature that you can be proud of.

_____

_____

_____

_____

_____

_____

_____

_____

_____

_____

Day Six Homework

Practice writing your email address and your street address.

_____

_____

_____

_____

_____

_____

_____

_____

_____

_____

_____

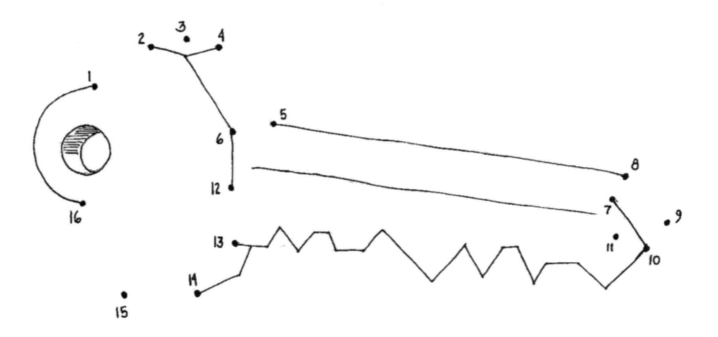

Extra Credit Week 1
Fun things List

You will do a lot of things in your lifetime! Finish this to-do list for some fun things you want to do this year:
1. Solve a mystery
2. Make a friend
3. Take stock
4. Buy a stock
5. Bake a cake

6. _____

7. _____

8. _____

9. _____

10. _____

WEEKLY COMPLIANCE SCORE:_____

To see how much of the handwriting work you did this week, go back through the week and give yourself 1 point for each exercise you did and 1 point for each homework activity you did. If you did them ALL, you earned 91 compliance points. If you did the EXTRA CREDIT activity, you get NINE extra points, for a total score of 100!

Aim for at least 85 points each week.

LETTERS-PER-MINUTE SELF-ASSESSMENT:_____

Open a book you have at your home to any page (use the same book each week), set a timer or stopwatch for 5 minutes, and begin to copy the sentences from the book. After five minutes, STOP writing. Count each individual letter you wrote. Divide the total number by 5. This is your **LETTERS-PER-MINUTE** writing speed. You can now do two things: (1) Check out the Handwriting for Heroes website for a list of normative, grade-level values to see how fast you are writing, and (2) Use this number to set a personal goal of improvement for next week's writing speed.

Handwriting for Heroes

Week Two

It is important to set realistic goals for myself.
Be specific and think about improving your speed,
legibility, endurance, commitment and motivation.
This week my handwriting goal is:

_____

_____

_____

_____

Exercise 1: Warm-ups

Write your first name in each box. Fill up the box. The variety of box sizes will force your brain to direct your hand to adjust its movements.

Day 1:

Day 2:

Day 3:

Day 4:

Day 5:

Day 6:

Day 7:

Exercise 2: Train in the rain

Copy two lines of these letters. Are you aware that when written in cursive, all five letters have loops above the lines?

llllllllll ffffffffff eeeeeee hhhhhhhh bbbbbbbb

lllllllllll ffffffffffff eeeeeeeeeee hhhhhhhhh bbbbbbbb

Day 1:

_____

_____

Day 2:

_____

_____

Day 3:

_____

_____

Day 4:

_____

_____

Day 5:

_____

_____

Day 6:

_____

_____

Day 7:

_____

Exercise 3: Range control

This exercise is about stretching and growing. Trace the following curvy-line:

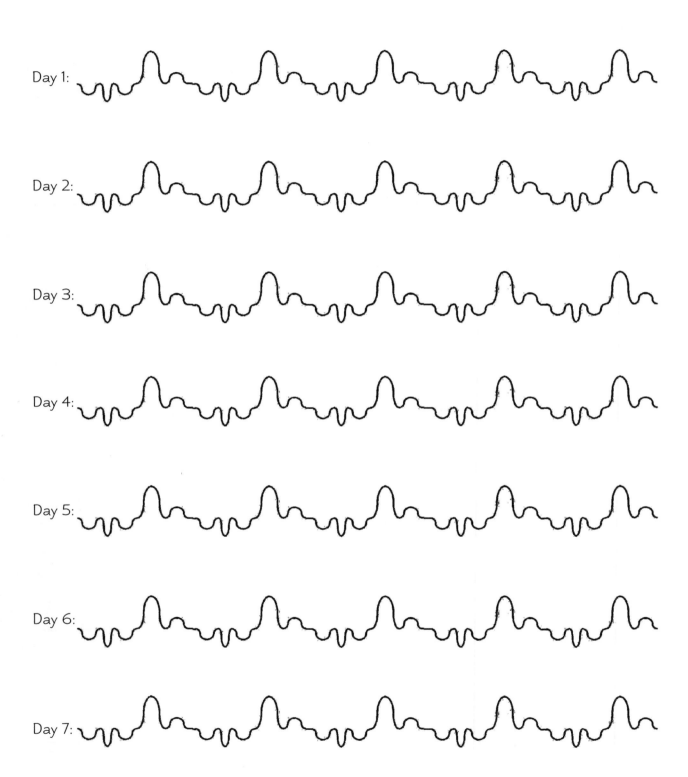

Day 1:

Day 2:

Day 3:

Day 4:

Day 5:

Day 6:

Day 7:

Exercise 4: Stretches

Use a pencil to fill in (shade) the shapes.

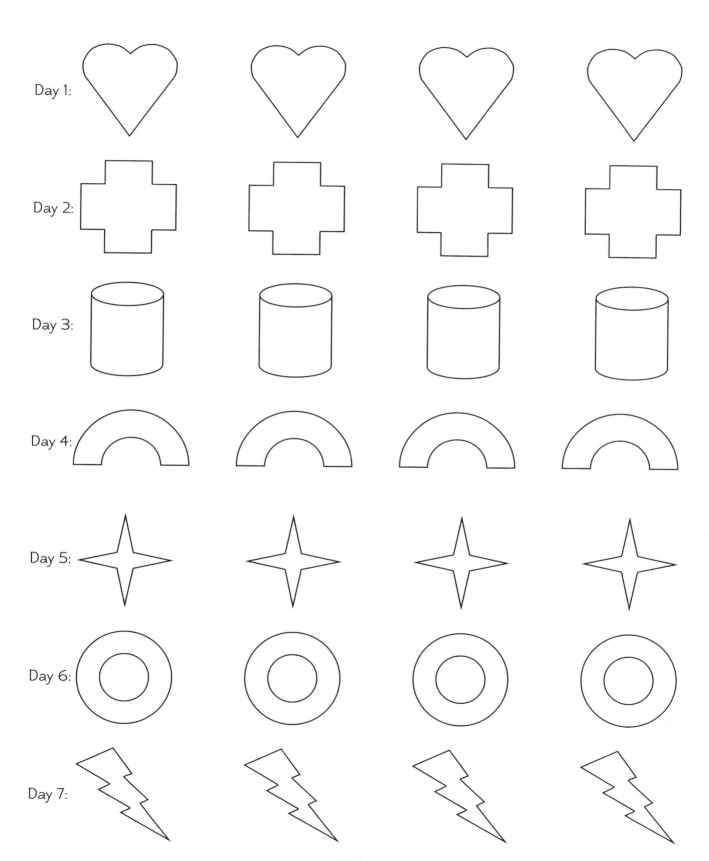

Day 1:

Day 2:

Day 3:

Day 4:

Day 5:

Day 6:

Day 7:

Exercise 5: Spit shine

Repetition and attention to details put the polishing touches on anything. In the military, that's what makes a good "spit shine". Write two lines of the following letter sequences:

ekhekhekhekhekhekhekhekhe flefleflefleflefleflefle

ekh ekh ekh ekh ekh ekh ekh ekh fle fle fle fle fle fle fle fle

Day 1: _____

_____

Day 2: _____

_____

Day 3: _____

_____

Day 4: _____

_____

Day 5: _____

_____

Day 6: _____

_____

Day 7: _____

_____

Exercise 6: Speed drills

Your brain is familiar with common letter sequences that are repeated in many English language words. Write two lines of the following letter sequences:

age age edge edge back back able able ing ing

age age edge edge back back able able ing ing

Day 1: _____

_____

Day 2: _____

_____

Day 3: _____

_____

Day 4: _____

_____

Day 5: _____

_____

Day 6: _____

_____

Day 7: _____

_____

Exercise 7: Boot lacing

This exercise features two words that use the letters we are focusing on this week, which, in cursive, require lifting your pen from the paper between words. Please remember to resume your slant once you resume writing. Copy two lines of the following:

like like like like half half half half

like like like like like   half half half half half

Day 1:

Day 2:

Day 3:

Day 4:

Day 5:

Day 6:

Day 7:

Exercise 8: In cadence

Cursive Learners: Trace the letters in the sentence below and on the following page.
Print Learners: Below the cursive example, write the sentence,

"Today I feel better than yesterday. I can't wait until tomorrow."

Day 1: *Today I feel better than yesterday. I can't wait until tomorrow.*

Day 2: *Today I feel better than yesterday. I can't wait until tomorrow.*

Day 3: *Today I feel better than yesterday. I can't wait until tomorrow.*

Day 4: Today I feel better than yesterday. I can't wait until tomorrow.

Day 5: Today I feel better than yesterday. I can't wait until tomorrow.

Day 6: Today I feel better than yesterday. I can't wait until tomorrow.

Day 7: Today I feel better than yesterday. I can't wait until tomorrow.

Exercise 9: Carbon copy

The following sentence contains every letter of the alphabet ... Write it two times.

Once upon a time, a zealous boy named Jack Frost gave his extra quarters away.

Once upon a time, a zealous boy named Jack Frost gave his extra quarters away.

Day 1: _____

_____

_____

Day 2: _____

_____

_____

Day 3: _____

_____

_____

Day 4: _____

_____

_____

Day 5: _____

_____

_____

Day 6: _____

_____

_____

Day 7: _____

_____

_____

Exercise 10: Steady at the Ready

This exercise helps you to combine straight line and loop letters. When you move between line and loop, pay careful attention not to lose your proper slant. Copy this sentence two times:

I seek freedom from negative thoughts.

I seek freedom from negative thoughts.

Day 1:

_____

_____

Day 2:

_____

_____

Day 3:

_____

_____

Day 4:

_____

_____

Day 5:

_____

_____

Day 6:

_____

_____

Day 7:

_____

_____

Exercise 11: Endurance training

NOW, neatness counts! . Are you keeping correct hand position and the same slant? Copy the one sentence below.

To become successful in life, remember that what you do today matters. To become successful in life, remember that what you do today matters.

Day 1:

_____

_____

Day 2:

_____

_____

Day 3:

_____

_____

Day 4:

_____

_____

Day 5:

_____

_____

Day 6:

_____

_____

Day 7:

_____

Exercise 12: Esprit de corps   Copy the following statement:

Do the following things this week: 1. Call a friend.
2. Read a book. 3. Take a nap.   Do the following things
this week: 1. Call a friend. 2. Read a book. 3. Take a nap.

*Review today's work and place a STAR next to today's best writing.

Day 1: _____

_____

Day 2: _____

_____

Day 3: _____

_____

Day 4: _____

_____

Day 5: _____

_____

Day 6: _____

_____

Day 7: _____

_____

Exercise 13: Mighty Mindset Exercise: *Improve* Your Signature Strengths

The Values in Action (VIA) Institute on Character created a classification system that is comprised of 24 character strengths that fall into 6 broad virtue categories.

Wisdom: Creativity, Curiosity, Judgment, Love of Learning, Perspective
Humanity: Love, Kindness, Social Intelligence
Justice: Teamwork, Fairness, Leadership
Transcendence: Appreciation of Beauty, Gratitude, Hope, Humor, Spirituality
Courage: Bravery, Perseverance, Honesty, Zest
Temperance: Forgiveness, Humility, Prudence, Self-Regulation

Each of us has all 24 of these character strengths, just in varying degrees. The VIA signature strengths survey was developed by Christopher Peterson, Ph.D. as a questionnaire that provides a rank order of these 24 character strengths. It is comprised of 120 questions and takes about 15 minutes to complete.

Once you have completed your VIA survey, you will receive a unique profile that ranks each of your 24 strengths. This tool is not intended to bring your focus to the character strengths that happen to fall lower on your list. Instead, this list should draw your attention to your top five strengths, which will be referred to as your *signature strengths*.

According to the research completed by positive psychologist Martin Seligman, participants who used one of their strengths in a new way for one week demonstrated increased happiness and decreased depressive symptoms. Learning what your signature strengths are can increase self-awareness and renew the importance of fostering personal happiness in your everyday life.

Your 13th exercise is on the next page!

Exercise 13:   Mighty Mindset Exercise: Improve Your Signature Strengths

Day 1: Take the VIA signature strengths survey online for free at http://www.viacharacter.org. Record you top 5 strengths on the space provided on days 2 and 3.

Day 2: List two ways you use each of these strengths in your life now:

_____

_____

Use one of your top five strengths in a NEW way each day for the rest of this week.

Day 3: Fill in the strength you focused on using today. How did you use this strength is a new way?

Strength: _____

I used this strength in a new way today by _____

Day 4: Fill in the strength you focused on using today. How did you use this strength is a new way?

Strength: _____

I used this strength in a new way today by _____

Day 5: Fill in the strength you focused on using today. How did you use this strength is a new way?

Strength: _____

I used this strength in a new way today by _____

Day 6: Fill in the strength you focused on using today. How did you use this strength is a new way?

Strength: _____

I used this strength in a new way today by _____

Day 7: Fill in the strength you focused on using today. How did you use this strength is a new way?

Strength: _____

I used this strength in a new way today by _____

_____

THERAPISTS' TIPS

PAPER POSITION

For the right hand dominant person,
the upper right hand corner of the paper is higher.

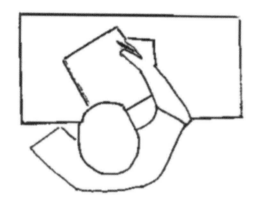

For the left hand dominant person,
the upper left hand corner of the paper is higher.

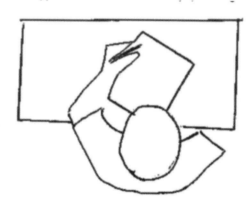

The writing hand should be below the line of handwriting in order to allow visualization. These paper positions encourage a neutral wrist position, which is biomechanically more efficient than a hooked position in the case of left hander's position.

Using a clipboard can be helpful to prevent the paper from wandering around and frustrating you. We prefer to use a clipboard over placing a non-skid material under the paper, unless the material is very thin, because you are less likely to puncture through the paper with a solid surface behind it. You may want to put nonskid material (like Dycem®) under the clipboard if you find the clipboard moving.

THERAPISTS' TIPS

Activities that develop the fine motor skills also required for writing

- Scissor use: start a scrapbook, clip coupons, do craft projects for yourself or with kids
- Use a hole punch: again there are some great decorative punches for craft projects
- Use small stamps for making your own cards or craft projects
- Use tweezers to pick up small objects, play the game Operation™, or ......remember the strawberry huller (I may be dating myself), but use this "large tweezers" to pull the tops off of strawberries and then enjoy your reward
- Play marbles, Chinese checkers, and Pick up sticks

WHEN TO PRACTICE?

- Ideally you will practice during a time when you can focus and feel relaxed. You can put calming music on to try to feel more relaxed.
- Take frequent breaks. Look up and do some stretches.
- Write at a reasonable pace. If you are rushed, you are more likely to get fatigued, cramping in your hand, and frustrated.

THE FURNITURE

Without furniture that fits you correctly, it will be very challenging for you to have good posture, and therefore a good foundation for your arm and hand to work from. So let's talk about how to choose a well fitting chair and desk.

Chair

The right chair will be at a height that allows your feet to rest flat on the ground with your knees bent at 90 degrees. The depth of the seat of the chair should come to 2" from the back of the knee when seated fully back in the chair. If the seat of the chair has the ability to tilt, tilt it downward approximately 10 degrees. This will encourage engagement of the abdominal muscles and spinal extension. The opposite tilt will tend to make you sit with a forward flexed position which is to be avoided. Some people prefer lumbar support, while others prefer low thoracic support. Try either and use which ever is more comfortable for you.

Desk

The height of the desk should allow you to write with your elbows flexed at 90 degrees. Some people are more comfortable with the desk 1-2" higher for writing. This is different than the recommended height for typing or keyboarding, which would be at a lower height with the elbows more open.

Try an inclined surface ("slant board")

Have you ever noticed and wondered why architects and designers often work on an inclined surface? Writing on an inclined surface inherently encourages you to write with your wrist in an extended position. The inclined position encourages better posture and allows for a better visual field. You can try this out by using a three ring binder, before you go out and buy a table top inclined writing surface. Inclining the surface 15 to 30 degrees is ideal. This may be a way to start practicing. You will also need to become proficient on a flat surface because many of our writing requirements out in the community are done on a flat surface. The board below is available at www.discountschoolsupply.com

To Slant or Not to Slant? That is the Question.

In school we were taught that cursive writing should slant 30 degrees to the right. We are given tools to measure our slant. Once we leave school and proceed to functioning in the adult world we notice that some people write vertically, some slant far to the right, and some even slant to the left. So what is correct? Our purpose in handwriting is to communicate, so what is correct is the approach that will allow for the clearest communication. Slant contributes to legibility and what is most important is for the slant to be consistent. Beyond consistency with slant the rest is personal style. We recommend any slant between vertical and 30 degrees of forward slant. You choose what is most comfortable for you.

You can check your consistency by drawing a straight line through the center of each letter from top to bottom. If all of these drawn lines are parallel, then your slant is consistent.

Consistent

Consistent

Inconsistent

Week Two: Homework for Heroes

Day 1: Write the days of the week and the months of the year. List the holidays and birthdays family and friends during each month. Use the sheet provided.

Day 2: Write a list for grocery shopping and errands. Number each item to practice writing numbers, too. This is a practical exercise, so you should write it on paper that you can take with you.

Day 3: Find a quote from a book or magazine that you would like to memorize. Copy it seven times on the sheet provided. Did you realize you will be memorizing lots of "affirmation statements" as you progress through this workbook?

Day 4: Write the names of your family on the family tree graph included in this week's homework section. WRITE NEATLY in cursive or print (your choice).

Day 5: Complete the Dot-to-Dot illustration on the following page.

Day 6: Complete the coloring page in this week's homework section. HAVE FUN!!

Day 7: This homework exercise is called "translation." Place 10 small items (e.g. coins, buttons, marbles, safety pins, paperclips) on a surface in front of you. Then, pick them up one at a time and keep them in your hand (don't drop any as you pick up the next item). Now, reverse the drill and place the items back on the surface, one at a time, without dropping any of these still in your hand.

Day One Homework

Write the days of the week on the first two lines. Then write the name of each month and follow it with that month's holidays and your friends and family members' birthdays.

Days of the week:

_____

_____

Write the months below:

Month one:

_____

Month two:

_____

Month three:

_____

Month four:

_____

Month five:

_____

Month six:

_____

Month seven:

_____

Month eight:

_____

Month nine:

_____

Month ten:

_____

Month eleven:

_____

Month twelve:

_____

Day Three Homework

Find a quote from a book or magazine that you would like to memorize. Copy it seven times.

1: _____

_____

2: _____

_____

3: _____

_____

4: _____

_____

5: _____

_____

6: _____

_____

7: _____

_____

Day Four Homework

Draw a family tree. Write the names of your family on it. WRITE NEATLY in cursive or in print.

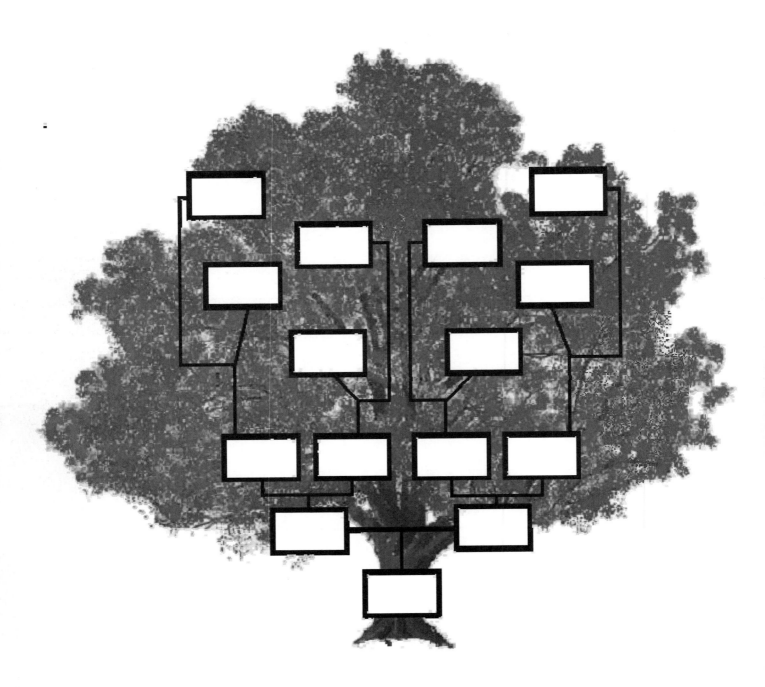

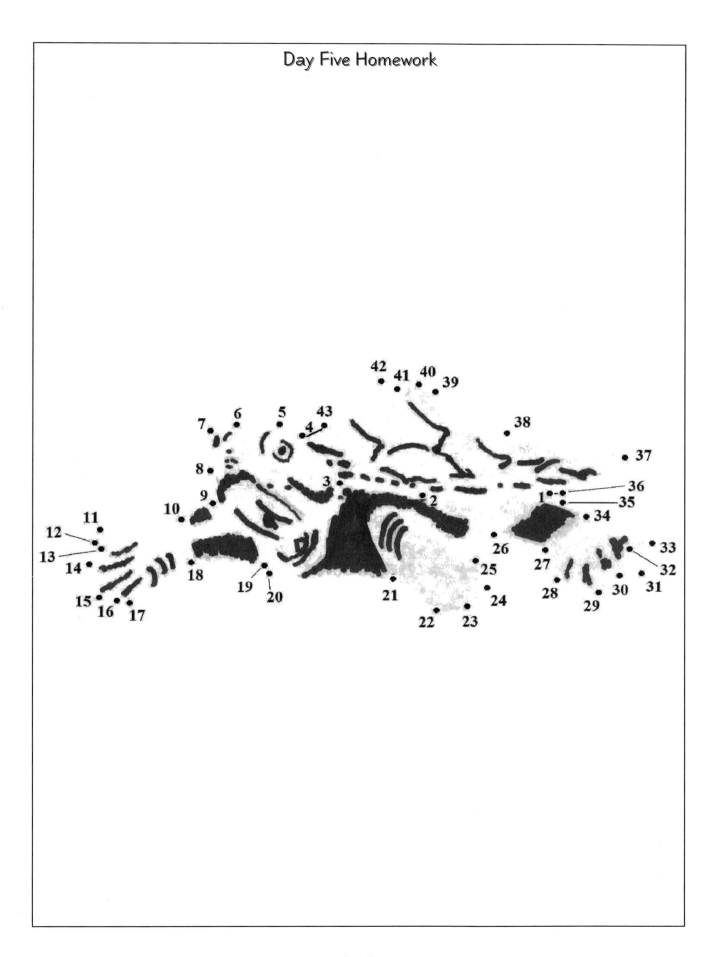

Color Code:
S - Red
B - Orange
P - Blue

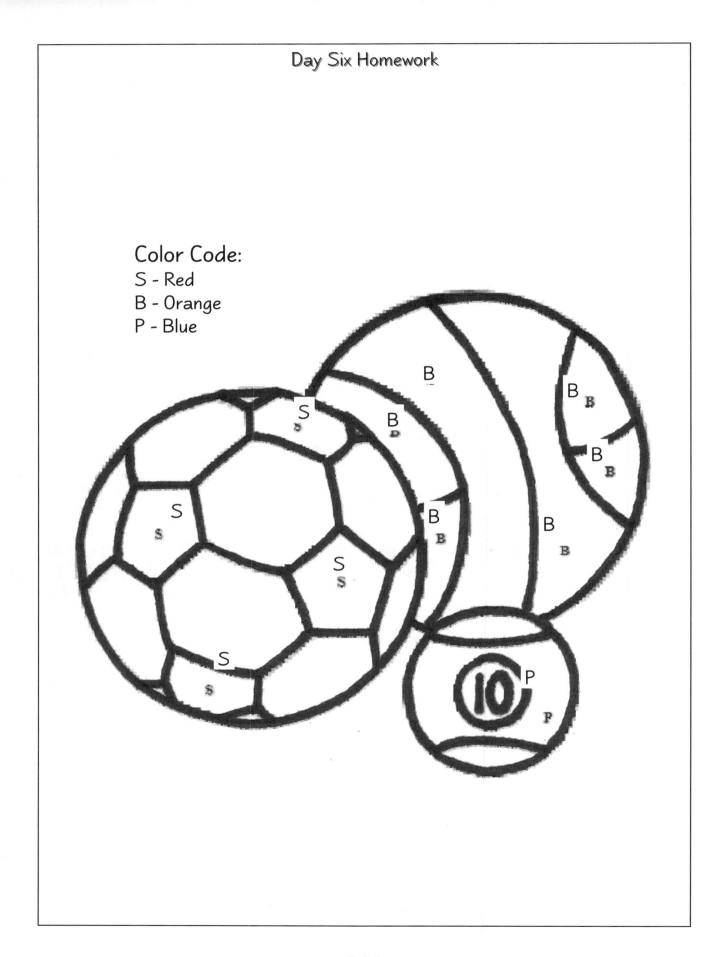

Extra Credit Week 2
Sports Fanatic

Fill in the sports chart below: (cursive or print)

Major City	Sport	Team Name
Pittsburgh	Football	
Baltimore	Baseball	
		Cowboys
		Wizards
		Celtics
Denver	Football	
San Francisco	Football	
Los Angeles	Baseball	
		Cavaliers
		Bulls
		Yankees
Green Bay	Football	
		Cubs
Kansas City	Football	
		Mets
Orlando	Basketball	
Chicago		
		Pirates
		Braves

WEEKLY COMPLIANCE SCORE_____

To see how much of the handwriting work you did this week, go back through the week and give yourself 1 point for each exercise you did and 1 point for each homework activity you did. If you did them ALL, you earned 91 compliance points. If you did the EXTRA CREDIT activity, you get NINE extra points, for a total score of 100!

Aim for at least 85 points each week.

LETTERS-PER-MINUTE SELF-ASSESSMENT:_____

Open a book you have at your home to any page (use the same book each week), set a timer or stopwatch for 5 minutes, and begin to copy the sentences from the book. After five minutes, STOP writing. Count each individual letter you wrote. Divide the total number by 5. This is your LETTERS-PER-MINUTE writing speed. You can now do two things: (1) Check out the Handwriting for Heroes website for a list of normative, grade-level values to see how fast you are writing, and (2) Use this number to set a personal goal of improvement for next week's writing speed.

Handwriting for Heroes

Week Three

It is important to set realistic goals for myself.
Be specific and think about improving your speed,
legibility, endurance, commitment and motivation.
This week my handwriting goal is:

_____

_____

_____

_____

Exercise 1: Warm-ups

Draw six circles, then make clocks out of them. Select a time for each clock, and write below the clock what that time of day represents to you and your current schedule.

Day 1:

Day 4:

Day 2:

Day 5:

Day 3:

Day 6:

Exercise 2: Train in the rain

Write two lines of the letters l t u p s and o:

iiiiiiiiiiiitttttttttttuuuuuu ppppppsssssssssssoooooooooooooo

iiiiiiiii ttttttttt uuuuuu ppppp ssssssssss ooooooooo

Day 1:

_____

_____

Day 2:

_____

_____

Day 3:

_____

_____

Day 4:

_____

_____

Day 5:

_____

_____

Day 6:

_____

_____

Day 7:

_____

_____

Exercise 3: Range control

This exercise is about stretching and growing. Trace the following curvy-line:

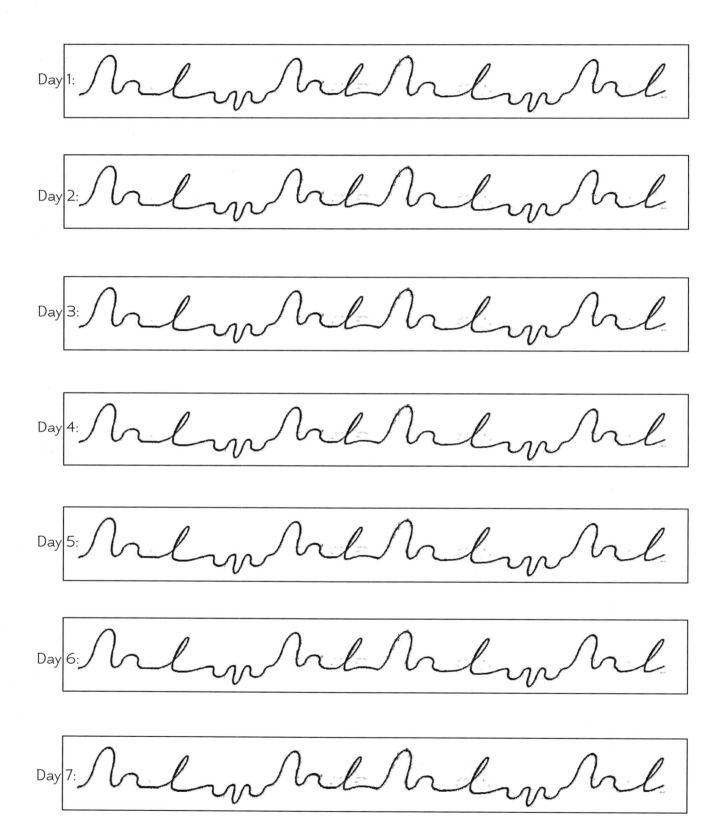

Day 1:

Day 2:

Day 3:

Day 4:

Day 5:

Day 6:

Day 7:

Exercise 4: Stretches

Using a pencil, fill in the stars.

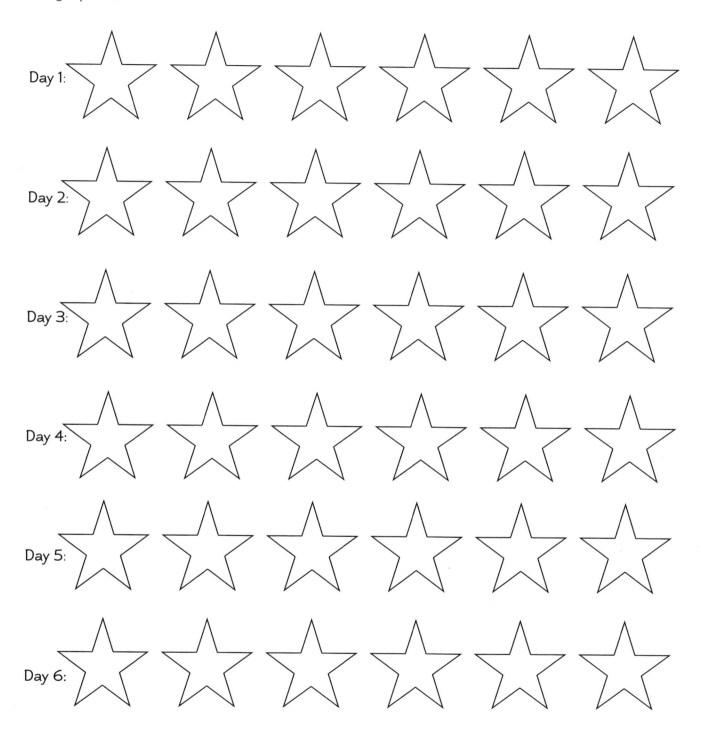

Day 1:

Day 2:

Day 3:

Day 4:

Day 5:

Day 6:

Day 7: Draw six stars free hand.

Exercise 5: Spit shine

Repetition and attention to details put the polishing touches on anything. In the military, that's what makes a good "spit shine". In the following exercises, copy two lines, keeping a consistent slant:

sitsitsitsitsitsitsitsitsitsit pourpourpourpourpour

sit sit sit sit sit sit pour pour pour pour pour

Day 1: _____

_____

Day 2: _____

_____

Day 3: _____

_____

Day 4: _____

_____

Day 5: _____

_____

Day 6: _____

_____

Day 7: _____

_____

3-6

Exercise 6: Speed drills

Write two lines of the following sets of letters (w, u, r, s, o). Move as quickly as you can. In this exercise, speed is more important than neatness.

wurso wurso wurso wurso wurso wurso wurso

wurso wurso wurso wurso wurso wurso wurso

Day 1:

_____

_____

Day 2:

_____

_____

Day 3:

_____

_____

Day 4:

_____

_____

Day 5:

_____

_____

Day 6:

_____

_____

Day 7:

_____

_____

Exercise 7: Boot lacing

Make X's in the boxes as shown in the example.

Day 1:

Day 2:

Day 3:

Day 4:

Day 5:

Day 6:

Day 7:

Exercise 8: In cadence

Cursive Learners: trace the letters in each word of the sentence by J.C. Maxwell
Print Learners: Below the cursive example, write the sentence,
"Nothing of value comes without sacrifice."

Day 1: *"Nothing of value comes without sacrifice."*

Day 2: *"Nothing of value comes without sacrifice."*

Day 3: *"Nothing of value comes without sacrifice."*

Day 4: *"Nothing of value comes without sacrifice."*

Day 5: *"Nothing of value comes without sacrifice."*

Day 6: *"Nothing of value comes without sacrifice."*

Day 7: *"Nothing of value comes without sacrifice."*

Exercise 9: Carbon copy

The following sentence contains every letter of the alphabet … really! So, this exercise is like writing your ABCs but you won't even know you've done it. It's the medicine-in-the-applesauce method of writing your ABCs.

When the crazy viper sneaked by, a big fox quickly jumped out of hiding.

When the crazy viper sneaked by a big fox quickly jumped out of hiding.

Day 1: _____

_____

Day 2: _____

_____

Day 3: _____

_____

Day 4: _____

_____

Day 5: _____

_____

Day 6: _____

_____

Day 7: _____

_____

Exercise 10: Steady at the Ready

During this exercise, you will be combining straight line and loop letters. When you move between line and loop, be careful not to lose your proper slant. Copy this sentence two times:

I can do anything I put my mind to.

I can do anything I put my mind to.

Day 1:

Day 2:

Day 3:

Day 4:

Day 5:

Day 6:

Day 7:

Exercise 11: Endurance training

Copy the sentence two times. NOW, neatness counts!

I will learn to write with my non-dominant hand; I will call it my "new-dominant" hand.

I will learn to write with my non-dominant hand, I will call it my new-dominant hand.

Day 1: _____

_____

Day 2: _____

_____

Day 3: _____

_____

Day 4: _____

_____

Day 5: _____

_____

Day 6: _____

_____

Day 7: _____

_____

Exercise 12: Esprit de corps

Copy the following sentence: *Today I will focus on myself and not regulate anybody else.*

Today I will focus on myself and not regulate anybody else.

Review today's work and place a STAR next to today's best writing.

Day 1: _____

_____

Day 2: _____

_____

Day 3: _____

_____

Day 4: _____

_____

Day 5: _____

_____

Day 6: _____

_____

Day 7: _____

_____

Exercise 13: Mighty Mindset Exercise: <u>G</u>ratitude

Being grateful is a personal attribute that indicates that you are appreciative and thankful to someone else. While it may be common to be grateful after receiving a gift, positive psychology focuses on the act of gratitude in regards to everyday events. In fact, expressing your gratitude in written form can encourage a more positive outlook on your personal life satisfaction and overall well-being.

This week you will be writing two letters of gratitude. Each of these letters will be written to different individuals to express your appreciation for something they have done for you; whether big or small. Avoid writing a 'thank you note' for a gift that you have received Challenge yourself to write expressively and with a positive demeanor.

Day 1:

Who are you writing your 1st letter of gratitude to?

_____

What event/act are you grateful for?

_____

_____

_____

How did this person's act of kindness make you feel?

_____

_____

_____

How has this act of kindness influenced your future?

_____

_____

_____

Exercise 13 (continued): Mighty Mindset Exercise: <u>G</u>ratitude

Day 2: Use Day 1's information and write your letter of gratitude.

Day 3: Re-read your letter of gratitude. Reflect on how you felt after writing this letter and remembering the positive event you wrote about. Either hand-deliver or mail your letter the recipient.

Day 4:
Who are you writing your 2nd letter of gratitude to?

_____

What event/act are you grateful for?

_____

How did this person's act of kindness make you feel?

_____

_____

_____

How has this act of kindness influenced your future?

_____

_____

_____

Day 5: Use the information you wrote out from Day 4 to write your second letter of gratitude.

Day 6: Re-read your letter of gratitude. Reflect on how you felt after writing this letter and remembering the positive event you wrote about. Either hand deliver or mail your letter the recipient.

Day 7: Reflect on a time that felt you that accomplished something as a result of your hard work and dedication. Write yourself a letter of gratitude to express how accomplishing that achievement made you feel. Make sure to give yourself the same recognition that you put into your other two letters of gratitude.

THERAPISTS' TIPS

HOW DO YOU HOLD THE PENCIL/PEN?

The optimal grasp is a dynamic tripod. This grasp includes:

- an extended wrist
- the wrist is not in a hooked position
- an open web space
- grasp is distal with the thumb, index, and middle in a triad
- the fingers move, controlling the pencil as opposed to the proximal joints
- the end of the writing device should point towards the shoulder

Why is it important to hold the writing device a certain way?

Use of the correct grasp pattern allows for the most efficient writing. You will write quickly and fluidly. Awkward grasp patterns can also lead to physical problems like carpal tunnel syndrome or overuse syndromes over time. If you have decreased use of one upper extremity, then you demand more of your uninvolved upper extremity. This already puts you at risk, so we want you to protect your arms and hands.

For left-handed writers:

For right-handed writers:

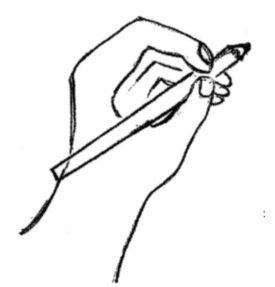

THERAPISTS' TIPS

For the left-handed writer, it may help to hold the writing device 1" or so higher to allow for better visualization of your writing and to decrease smudging. If you feel like you have less control with a higher grasp, go back to holding lower until your control improves with practice.

Another option that offers more stability is the *dynamic quadropod grasp*. This grasp includes:

- Grasping distally with opposition of the thumb, index, middle, and ring fingers
- An open web space
- The fingers move during writing

Both of these grasp patterns require separation of sides of the hand and distal digital control.

Some exercises to develop separation of sides of the hand are:

- Holding an eraser with the ring and small fingers while picking up coins off of the table
- Holding an eraser with the ring and small fingers while erasing a line
- Holding an eraser with the ring and small fingers while pulling a piece of yarn towards you using your thumb, index, and middle fingers
- Pick up a handful of marbles one by one, then drop them out of the small finger side of the hand, one by one

Exercises to develop distal digital control include:

- Spinning a top
- Twisting a cap on and off a small bottle
- Rolling putty into small balls
- Pushing thread through straws
- Sewing, knitting, and crocheting
- Spinning nuts on and off of bolts

To develop strength in your proximal muscles, trunk, and specifically, wrist extension:

- Practice writing on a vertical surface
- A chalkboard will provide more resistance
- A dry-erase board will provide less resistance

To develop general upper body strength:

- If you belong to a gym, ask a trainer to develop a program that targets the upper back, shoulders, and upper arms
- Pulleys and Theraband exercises can be modified to be used with both arms when one hand has limited or no grasp.
- Weightbearing on your forearms will activate muscles of the back and chest. You could do this laying on your stomach with your arms on a pillow while reading or watching TV.

Week Three: Homework for Heroes

Day 1: Write information on the news, weather, and sports on the following page.

Day 2: Write the names and phone numbers of 10 of your closest friends and families. Use the data sheet in this section. You could also try writing it on an index card for handy reference.

Day 3: Complete the calendar grid. This exercise will help you write smaller letters/words in cursive.

Day 4: Complete the coloring page with any variety of colors. HAVE FUN!!

Day 5: Complete the dot-to-dot exercise on the following page.

Day 6: Complete your personal data sheet.

Day 7: Use the checkbook ledger to solve a practical math problem.
Navy Captain James Applesauce is paid $2,244.00 twice a month (on the 1st and the 15th). This month he wrote eight checks. What was his checkbook balance at the end of the January?

    January 3, #101: Mortgage Matters for $1,215.00
    January 6, #102: Everyone's Church for $220.00
    January 10, #103: Electrical Energy for $32.00
    January 11, #104: Wash-my-car-Wendy for $17.50
    January 13, #105: Everyone's Church for $220.00
    January 22, #106: Pizza Delight for $24.92
    January 26, #107: What's-A-Matter-University for $78.50
    January 30, #108: Gas Guzzler's Corner Store for $52.18

You can see if your answer is correct by going online: www.handwritingforheros.com

Truthfully, we're more interested in your ability to write neatly than to do the math problem, but we recognize that legibly writing numbers helps you keep your personal checkbook in order!

Day One Homework

Read a newspaper or website for information to write about news, weather, and sports.

News:

Weather:

Sports:

Day Two Homework

Write down the names, email addresses, and phone numbers of ten friends and family members. This is a good time to practice printing.

Name	Email Address	Phone Number

Day Three Homework

Month/Year: _____

Write the days of the week across the shaded boxes, then write the numbers in the upper left corner of each of the large boxes.

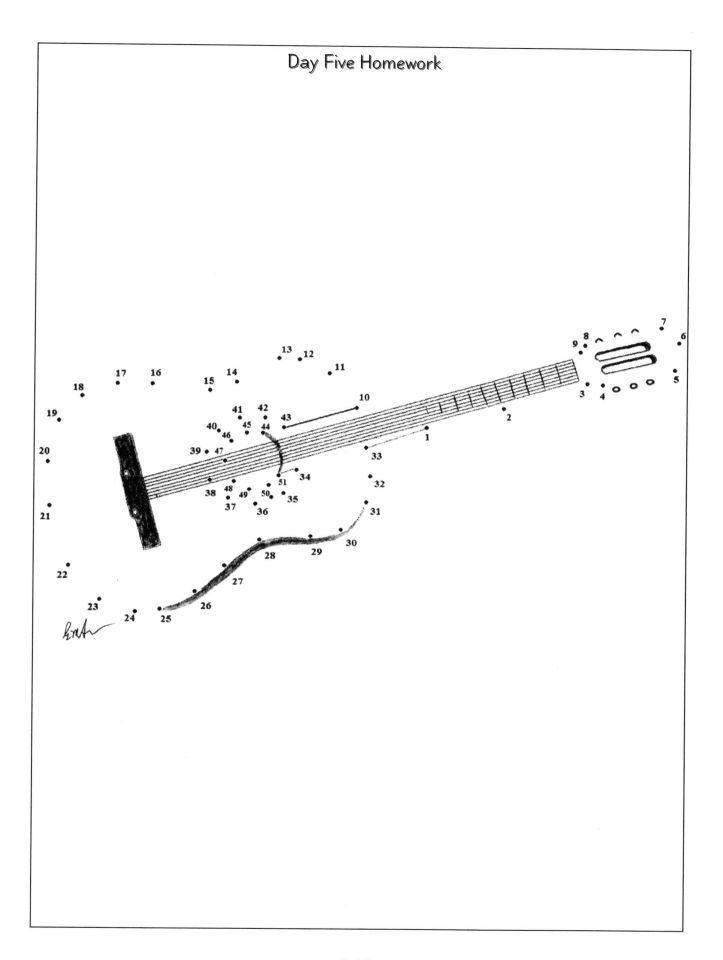

Day Six Homework

Fill in your information on this personal data sheet.

Name:

Age:

Favorite color:

Favorite food:

Favorite restaurant:

Favorite book:

Favorite movie:

Last movie you watched:

Favorite type of music:

Favorite music group/band:

Favorite television program:

Favorite sport:

Day Seven Homework

Use the checkbook ledger to enter deposits and checks and solve the following math problem (hint: all lines are required)

Navy Captain James Applesauce is paid $2,244.00 twice a month (on the 1st and the 15th). This month he wrote eight checks. What was his checkbook balance at the end of the January?

January 3, #101: Mortgage Matters for $1,215.00

January 6, #102: Everyone's Church for $220.00

January 10, #103: Electrical Energy for $32.00

January 11, #104: Wash-my-car-Wendy for $17.50

January 13, #105: Everyone's Church for $220.00

January 22, #106: Pizza Delight for $24.92

January 26, #107: What's-A-Matter-University for $78.50

January 30, #108: Gas Guzzler's Corner Store for $52.18

Check #	Date	Description of transaction	Debit (-) or Money Spent	Credit (+), or Deposits	Balance
	1/1	Beginning Balance			51.25
	1/2	Deposit (paycheck)		2,244.00	
	1/15	Deposit (paycheck)		2,244.00	

You can see if your answer is correct by going online: www.handwritingforheros.com

Truthfully, we're more interested in your ability to write neatly than to do the math problem, but we recognize that legibly writing numbers helps you keep your personal checkbook in order!

Extra Credit Week 3
Catchy phrases
Complete each familiar catch phrase below.

Don't put the _____ in front of the horse.

You are the _____ of my eye.

Don't count your _____ before they hatch.

It is raining like _____ and _____ outside.

Don't judge a _____ by its _____.

A _____ in time saves a dime.

There is a _____ _____ in every cloud.

When it rains, it _____.

When the goin' gets tough, the tough get _____.

Don't put all your _____ in one _____.

WEEKLY COMPLIANCE SCORE_____

To see how much of the handwriting work you did this week, go back through the week and give yourself 1 point for each exercise you did and 1 point for each homework activity you did. If you did them ALL, you earned 91 compliance points. If you did the EXTRA CREDIT activity, you get NINE extra points, for a total score of 100!

Aim for at least 85 points each week.

LETTERS-PER-MINUTE SELF-ASSESSMENT:_____

Open a book you have at your home to any page (use the same book each week), set a timer or stopwatch for 5 minutes, and begin to copy the sentences from the book. After five minutes, STOP writing. Count each individual letter you wrote. Divide the total number by 5. This is your LETTERS-PER-MINUTE writing speed. You can now do two things: (1) Check out the Handwriting for Heroes website for a list of normative, grade-level values to see how fast you are writing, and (2) Use this number to set a personal goal of improvement for next week's writing speed.

Handwriting for Heroes

Week Four

It is important to set realistic goals for myself.
Be specific and think about improving your speed,
legibility, endurance, commitment and motivation.
This week my handwriting goal is:

_____

_____

_____

_____

Exercise 1: Warm-ups

Write numbers 0 to 10 in each of the boxes below:

Day 1:

Day 2:

Day 3:

Day 4:

Day 5:

Day 6:

Day 7:

Exercise 2: Train in the rain

Write two lines of the letters "n, y and m, v." **Cursive Learners**, keep your pen on the paper. Lift it only move to the next line. Are you being consistent with your slant!?

nnnnnyyyyyyyynnnnnnnnvvvvvvmmm

nnnn yyyy nnnn vvvvv mmmm nnn yyy vvv mmm

Day 1:

_____

Day 2:

_____

Day 3:

_____

Day 4:

_____

Day 5:

_____

Day 6:

_____

Day 7:

_____

Exercise 3: Range control

This exercise is about stretching and growing. Trace the following curvy-line:

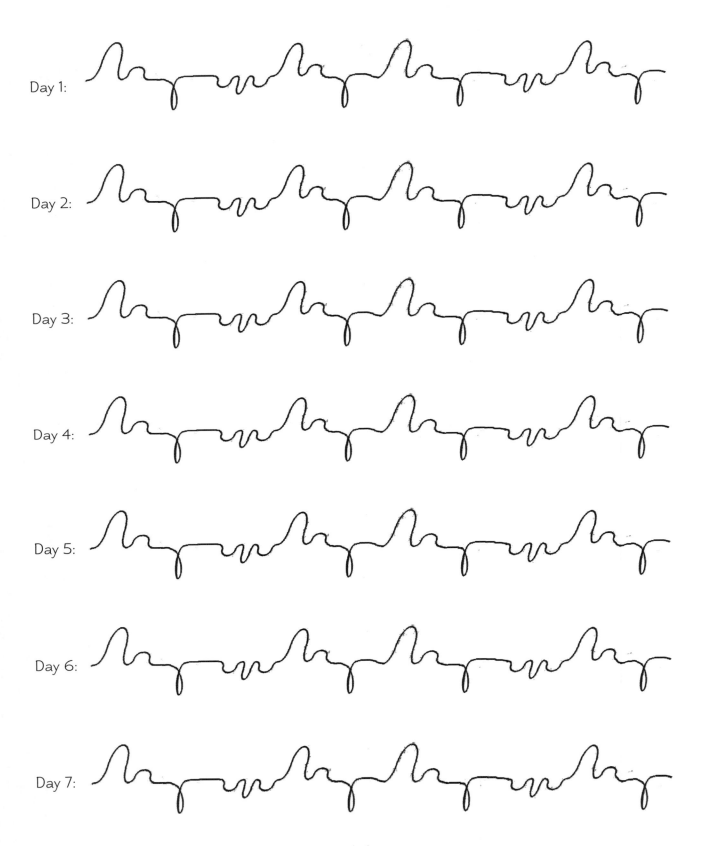

Day 1:

Day 2:

Day 3:

Day 4:

Day 5:

Day 6:

Day 7:

Exercise 4: Stretches

Write the months of the year. **Cursive Learners,** how consistent are your loops and the slants?

January February March April May June July August September October November December

January February March April May June July August September October November December

Day 1:

Day 2:

Day 3:

Day 4:

Day 5:

Day 6:

Day 7:

Exercise 5: Spit shine

Repetition and attention to details put the polishing touches on anything. In the military, that's what makes a good "spit shine". Write two lines of these letters each day:

yyyyyyyyyyyyyy,   mmmmmmmm

yyyyyyyyyyyyyyy   mmmmmmmmmmmm

Day 1: _____

_____

Day 2: _____

_____

Day 3: _____

_____

Day 4: _____

_____

Day 5: _____

_____

Day 6: _____

_____

Day 7: _____

_____

4-6

Exercise 6: Speed drills

Write the letters *e, o, m, n, v,* and *y* in the combined words *ney* and *move*, as shown below. **Cursive Learners,** did you notice that all the letters start with a upward motion?

ney ney ney ney move move move move

ney ney ney ney ney move move move move move

Day 1:
_____

_____

Day 2:
_____

_____

Day 3:
_____

_____

Day 4:
_____

_____

Day 5:
_____

_____

Day 6:
_____

_____

Day 7:
_____

_____

Exercise 7: Boot lacing

Cursive Learners: Using a pencil, trace inside the bubble letters of the words in the sentence.
Print Learners: Below the cursive example, write the sentence:

Handwriting is fun for me!

Day 1: *Handwriting is fun for me!*

Day 2: *Handwriting is fun for me!*

Day 3: *Handwriting is fun for me!*

Day 4: *Handwriting is fun for me!*

Day 5: *Handwriting is fun for me!*

Day 6: *Handwriting is fun for me!*

Day 7: *Handwriting is fun for me!*

Exercise 8: In cadence

Cursive Learners: Trace the letters in each word of the sentence.
Print Learners: Below the cursive example, write,

Learning a skill takes time and energy. There are many things I would like to learn.

Day 1: Learning a skill takes time and energy. There are many things I would like to learn.

Day 2: Learning a skill takes time and energy. There are many things I would like to learn.

Day 3: Learning a skill takes time and energy. There are many things I would like to learn.

Print Learners: Write the sentence below the cursive example:

Learning a skill takes time and energy. There are many things I would like to learn.

Day 4: *Learning a skill takes time and energy. There are many things I would like to learn.*

Day 5: *Learning a skill takes time and energy. There are many things I would like to learn.*

Day 6: *Learning a skill takes time and energy. There are many things I would like to learn.*

Day 7: *Learning a skill takes time and energy. There are many things I would like to learn.*

Exercise 9: Carbon copy

The following sentence contains every letter of the alphabet Write the sentence two times.

The zookeeper fed the busy aardvark while Megan quickly fixed the jaguar's cage.

The zookeeper fed the busy aardvark while Megan quickly fixed the jaguar's cage.

Day 1:

_____

_____

Day 2:

_____

_____

Day 3:

_____

_____

Day 4:

_____

_____

Day 5:

_____

_____

Day 6:

_____

_____

Day 7:

_____

Exercise 10: Steady at the Ready

Each day as you do this exercise, you will work on combining straight line and loop letters. When you move between line and loop, please be careful to keep your proper slant. Write the following sentence two times:

Focus on being positive and having a great day.

Focus on being positive and having a great day.

Day 1: _____

_____

Day 2: _____

_____

Day 3: _____

_____

Day 4: _____

_____

Day 5: _____

_____

Day 6: _____

_____

Day 7: _____

_____

Exercise 11: Endurance training

Striving for neatness, copy the sentence below (attributed to Charles Lindbergh).

"Success is not measured by what a man accomplishes but by the opposition he has encountered."

"Success is not measured by what a man accomplishes but by the opposition he has encountered."

Day 1:

_____

_____

Day 2:

_____

_____

Day 3:

_____

_____

Day 4:

_____

_____

Day 5:

_____

_____

Day 6:

_____

_____

Day 7:

_____

_____

Exercise 12: Esprit de corps   Copy the following sentence:

Abraham Lincoln said, "Most people are about as happy as they make up their minds to be."

Abraham Lincoln said, "Most people are about as happy as they make up their minds to be."

*Review today's work and place a STAR next to today's best writing.

Day 1:

Day 2:

Day 3:

Day 4:

Day 5:

Day 6:

Day 7:

Exercise 13: Mighty Mindset Exercise: <u>H</u>appiness Advantage

Which comes first, happiness or success?

Think about a time when you started a new job. Typically we feel happiness and enthusiasm for this opportunity, and that motivates us to work hard. We then strive for success in this role. After a few months on the job we can start to feel the stress of the deadlines and experience fatigue or a sense of burden. It is in this moment that we tell ourselves that little white lie, "when I get promoted, things will be better... then I'll be happy".

Typically in our society the formula for happiness is to work hard, then you'll be successful....and THEN you'll be happy. The problem is if the standard for happiness comes after success, then every time you succeed at something that benchmark changes.

According to positive psychologist Shawn Achor, we need to reverse the order of the formula and create a 'Happiness Advantage'. This can be done by cultivating happiness in the midst of your everyday activities through a positive mindset; meaning that our happiness does not have to be dependent on our external environment and success. Instead it can be achieved through training our brain to acknowledge our daily successes and positive moments in each day.

This week, train your brain to broaden and build on daily positive experiences. Doing this teaches your brain to release chemicals like serotonin and dopamine that can create a positive mindset. These chemicals also help to counteract the chemical effects that can occur from stress, such as excessive cortisol.

Take five minutes each day this week to write down specific details about one positive experience from that day. To broaden and build on this event reflect on the following questions:
1. How did this good thing happen?
2. What strengths did I apply during this event?
3. What does this positive event mean to you?
4. How does this experience influence your future?

Day 1: _____

_____

_____

Take five minutes each day this week to write down specific details about one positive experience from that day. To broaden and build on this event, reflect on the following questions:

- How did this good thing happen?
- What strengths did I apply during this event?
- What does this positive event mean to you?
- How does this experience influence your future?

Day 2: _____

_____

_____

Day 3: _____

_____

_____

Day 4: _____

_____

_____

Day 5: _____

_____

_____

Day 6: _____

_____

_____

Day 7: _____

_____

THERAPISTS' TIPS

POSTURE

We all know that standing on a three-legged chair to change a light bulb is a disaster waiting to happen. It is important to have a solid base under us when tackling a task that requires us to challenge our skills. This applies to learning to change hand dominance for handwriting. Your posture is your base for handwriting. So we will talk about posture. Remember how our teachers and our parents reminded us to sit up straight? Well, here we go again.

Your chair and your desk will dictate much of how you sit; however even the best fitting furniture will not fix poor posture that is the result of poor muscle condition and learned behavior. Regular exercise and repetitive correction of poor posture will gradually lead to naturally good posture. Good sitting posture is sitting tall with your shoulders back. Stretch the top of your head towards the ceiling. Your weight should be distributed evenly over both hips. Your knees should be bent at 90 degrees and your feet flat on the floor. If you are unsure of what good posture looks or feels like, you may benefit from a visit to an occupational or physical therapist who specializes in body mechanics and ergonomics.

In order to provide your new dominant hand with a solid, stable trunk to work off of, we should start with a good chair. This chair should be a height that allows the knees to be bent at 90 degrees and the feet are flat on the floor. The hips should be bent slightly more than 90 degrees to encourage extension of the spine and facilitation of the abdominal muscles. It would be best to start with a chair that is not on wheels or that rotates. As your skills improve you can change to a more mobile chair if you wish.

The height of the desk should allow the elbows to bend at 90 degrees or slightly more open when the hand is resting on the paper.

Here are some stretches to do in between exercises to relax tight muscles and to encourage good posture. **Do these exercises gently and do not push the exercise to the point of pain or numbness:**

1. Shoulder rolls backwards
Shoulder blades should come gently backwards and down.
Hold this stretch for 10 seconds, repeat 5 times.
Avoid pushing chin out.

4-17

2. Neck stretches

Look down at the floor, stretching the back of the neck. Hold for 5 seconds, repeat 10 times.

Gently bring chin back and lengthen neck. Hold 5 seconds, repeat 10 times.

Bring left ear to left shoulder, hold 5 seconds, then bring right ear to right shoulder, hold 5 seconds. Repeat 10 times. Be cautious not to rotate head.

3. Wrist stretches

Using a wall, stretch wrist flexors by gently pushing wrist back. Hold for 10 seconds, repeat 3 times. Using the wall, stretch wrist extensors by gently pushing wrist bent. Hold for 10 seconds, repeat 3 times.

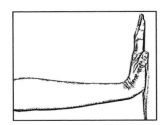 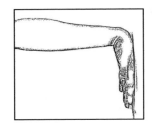

4. Finger stretches (abduction/adduction)

Stretch fingers wide apart, hold for 5 seconds, relax and bring fingers together, repeat 5 times.

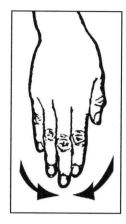
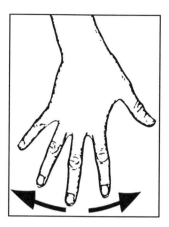

LIGHTING

It is a good idea to use bright light when working on close focusing with your eyes. Fluorescent bulbs spread light over large areas without glare. Other sources of glare may be working on a shiny surface or if your fixture is clear glass. Try working on a matte surface and using opaque shades or covers. The light should come from the left and slightly in front of you if you are right handed or from the right and slightly in front of you if you are left handed to avoid shadows. You do not want to see a reflection of the bulb on the paper.

Writing set up for writing right handed. The light would be on the right for someone writing left handed.

If you are working for a longer period of time you can rest your eyes by looking up and focusing on an object that is a middle or long distance away for a few minutes.

Week Four: Homework for Heroes

Day 1: Fidget with a pen and its cap. Place the cap on and off the pen and rotate the pen end to end to place the cap on the both ends of the pen without dropping the pen or the cap. This assignment you should while watching television so that you learn to do it without watching your hand move. Your hand is gaining skill and coordination without needing your eyes to watch its motions.

Day 2: Complete the budget worksheet on the corresponding page in this week's homework section.

Day 3: Write a letter to a friend or family member. Tell them all about yourself and what you've been busy with lately. Tell them about your plans for the next few months and what you are looking forward to doing when the season changes.

Day 4: Complete the coloring page in this week's homework section. HAVE FUN!!

Day 5: Complete the Dot-To-Dot figure in this week's homework section.

Day 6: Write yourself a "to-do" list. Since this is a practical exercise, write it on paper that you can place where you can see it and check off tasks as you complete them.

Day 7: Practice your signature. Use the space provided in the homework section. Write it both small and large. You will be asked to sign your name many times; how big or small you write it will depend on where you're signing it.

Day Two Homework

Monthly income: $ _____ + _____ + _____ = _____

(total income)

(add the following expenses and write the total on the line below)

Electric: $ _____

Water: $ _____

Gas: $ _____

Vehicle expenses: $ _____

Mortgage/rent: $ _____

Garbage: $ _____

Groceries/food: $ _____

Phone: $ _____

Electronic services
(tv, computer): $ _____

Routine monthly expenses: $ _____

Money available after paying for
routine expenses: $ _____

Write down what you want to do with your "leftover" money:

_____

_____

_____

_____

_____

_____

Day Seven Homework

Practice your signature by writing it as many times as you can. This one is for you, Print Learners!

_____

_____

_____

_____

_____

_____

_____

_____

_____

_____

_____

Extra Credit Week 4
Animal Attractions

In the box on the right column, write the name of an animal that starts with each letter in the word **"A-N-I-M-A-L" (cursive or printing)**

A (example: *ant*)	
N (example: newt)	
I (example: *iguana*)	
M (example: mouse)	
A (example: *aardvark*)	
L (example: lizard)	

WEEKLY COMPLIANCE SCORE_____

To see how much of the handwriting work you did this week, go back through the week and give yourself 1 point for each exercise you did and 1 point for each homework activity you did. If you did them ALL, you earned 91 compliance points. If you did the EXTRA CREDIT activity, you get NINE extra points, for a total score of 100!

Aim for at least 85 points each week.

LETTERS-PER-MINUTE SELF-ASSESSMENT:_____

Open a book you have at your home to any page (use the same book each week), set a timer or stopwatch for 5 minutes, and begin to copy the sentences from the book. After five minutes, STOP writing. Count each individual letter you wrote. Divide the total number by 5. This is your LETTERS-PER-MINUTE writing speed. You can now do two things: (1) Check out the Handwriting for Heroes website for a list of norma- tive, grade-level values to see how fast you are writing, and (2) Use this number to set a personal goal of improvement for next week's writing speed.

Handwriting for Heroes

Week Five

It is important to set realistic goals for myself.
Be specific and think about improving your speed,
legibility, endurance, commitment and motivation.
This week my handwriting goal is:

_____

_____

_____

_____

Exercise 1: Warm-ups

Write your last name in each of the boxes, adjusting the size to completely fill them. The variation in the box sizes will force your brain to tell your hand to adjust its movements.

Day 1:

Day 2:

Day 3:

Day 4:

Day 5:

Day 6:

Day 7:

Exercise 2: Train in-the-rain

Copy two lines of letters. **Cursive Learners:** have fun with the lower, "raindrop" loops.
Print Learners, have fun with the "sharp edges"

ȝȝȝȝȝȝȝȝȝȝȝȝȝȝȝȝȝȝȝȝȝȝȝȝqqqqqqqqqqqqqqqqqqqq

zzzzzzzzzzzzzzzzzzzzzzzz qqqqqqqqqqqqqqqqqqqq

Day 1: _____

_____

Day 2: _____

_____

Day 3: _____

_____

Day 4: _____

_____

Day 5: _____

_____

Day 6: _____

_____

Day 7: _____

_____

Exercise 3: Range control

This exercise is about stretching and growing. Trace the following curvy line pattern:

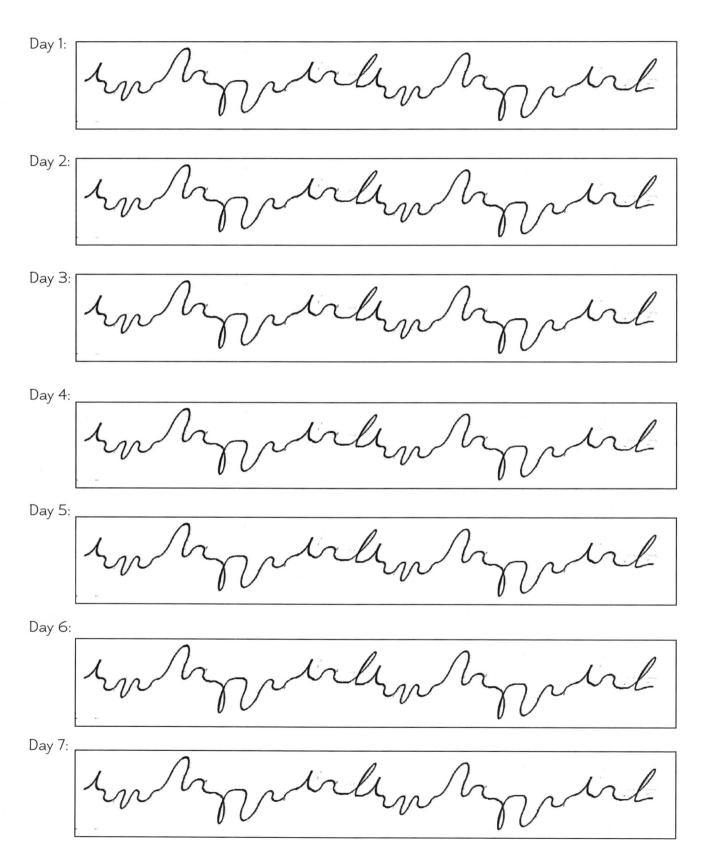

Day 1:

Day 2:

Day 3:

Day 4:

Day 5:

Day 6:

Day 7:

Exercise 4: Stretches

Copy two lines of two letter combinations:

xoxoxoxoxoxoxooxoxoxo quququququququ

xoxo xoxo xoxo xoxo ququ ququ ququ ququ

Day 1:
_____

_____

Day 2:
_____

_____

Day 3:
_____

_____

Day 4:
_____

_____

Day 5:
_____

_____

Day 6:
_____

_____

Day 7:
_____

Exercise 5: "Spit shine"

Repetition and attention to detail put the polishing touches on anything. In the military, that's what makes a good "spit shine." Write two lines of the continuous x, z, and q combinations:

xzqxzqxzqxzqxzqxzqxzqxzqxzqxzqxzqxzq

xzq xzq xzq xzq xzq xzq xzq xzq xzq xzq xzq xzq

Day 1:

_____

_____

Day 2:

_____

_____

Day 3:

_____

_____

Day 4:

_____

_____

Day 5:

_____

_____

Day 6:

_____

_____

Day 7:

_____

_____

Exercise 6: Speed drills

In this exercise speed is more important than neatness. Write two lines of the letter combination. Move as quickly as you can.

ezeque ezeque ezeque ezeque ezeque ezeque ezeque

ezeque ezeque ezeque ezeque ezeque ezeque ezeque

Day 1:
_____

_____

Day 2:
_____

_____

Day 3:
_____

_____

Day 4:
_____

_____

Day 5:
_____

_____

Day 6:
_____

_____

Day 7:
_____

_____

Exercise 7: "Boot lacing"

Cursive Learners: Using a pencil, trace inside the bubble letters of the words.
Print Learners: Write the sentence below the cursive example:

Things are looking up for me!

Day 1: *Things are looking up for me!*

Day 2: *Things are looking up for me!*

Day 3: *Things are looking up for me!*

Day 4: *Things are looking up for me!*

Day 5: *Things are looking up for me!*

Day 6: *Things are looking up for me!*

Day 7: *Things are looking up for me!*

Exercise 8: In cadence

Cursive Learners: Keeping your pen on the paper, trace the letters of each word in the sentences.
Print Learners: Below the cursive example, write the sentences:

Each time I do this exercise, I get better and better. I will stick with it!

Day 1: *Each time I do this exercise, I get better and better. I will stick with it!*

Day 2: *Each time I do this exercise, I get better and better. I will stick with it!*

Day 3: *Each time I do this exercise, I get better and better. I will stick with it!*

Print Learners: Write the sentences below the cursive example:

Each time I do this exercise, I get better and better. I will stick with it!

Day 4: *Each time I do this exercise, I get better and better. I will stick with it!*

Day 5: *Each time I do this exercise, I get better and better. I will stick with it!*

Day 6: *Each time I do this exercise, I get better and better. I will stick with it!*

Day 7: *Each time I do this exercise, I get better and better. I will stick with it!*

Exercise 9: Carbon copy

The following sentence contains every letter of the alphabet …no surprising you by now!

Queen Victoria always looked on the clearance rack for wide-bottom jeans with extra zippers.

Queen Victoria always looked on the clearance rack for wide-bottomed jeans with extra zippers.

Day 1:

_____

_____

Day 2:

_____

_____

Day 3:

_____

_____

Day 4:

_____

_____

Day 5:

_____

_____

Day 6:

_____

_____

Day 7:

_____

_____

Exercise 10: Steady at the Ready

Common words or strings of letters are used in much of our writing. Write two lines. Work as fast as you can while maintaining a consistent slant.

ful ful ful be be be ance ance ance ere ere ere

ful ful ful be be be ance ance ance ere ere ere

Day 1: _____

_____

Day 2: _____

_____

Day 3: _____

_____

Day 4: _____

_____

Day 5: _____

_____

Day 6: _____

_____

Day 7: _____

_____

Exercise 11: Endurance training

Copy the sentence below. NOW, neatness counts!

Francis Bacon said, "By far, the best proof is experience."

Francis Bacon said, "By far, the best proof is experience."

Day 1:

Day 2:

Day 3:

Day 4:

Day 5:

Day 6:

Day 7:

Exercise 12: Esprit de corps

Copy the following sentence twice.

Spend time thinking about pleasant memories.

Spend time thinking about pleasant memories.

*Review today's work and place a STAR next to today's best writing.

Day 1:

Day 2:

Day 3:

Day 4:

Day 5:

Day 6:

Day 7:

Exercise 13: Mighty Mindset Exercise: Three Good Things

The three good things exercise will train your brain to examine and expand on positive events that happen in your everyday life. Just like you are practicing to transfer your hand dominance, you have to also practice training your brain to be positive.

The familiar saying 'you can't teach an old dog new tricks' does not apply in positive psychology. Our brain adapts to a change in our habits and can be 'rewired' to create new neural pathways through repetition. Meaning that writing down good things that happen to you each day can actually train your brain to be more aware of positive experiences more than negative ones. By re-experiencing these positive events, it can train your brain to release neural chemicals that foster a sense of well-being and lead to a positive feeling.

Reflect on each day this week and write down three good things that happened to you. These can be small events (a nice text message, a cookie with lunch, taking the elevator to the top floor without stopping) or larger events (visit from a friend, good news from the doctor).

Day 1:

_____

_____

_____

Day 2:

_____

_____

_____

Exercise 13: (continued) Mighty Mindset Exercise: <u>T</u>hree Good Things

Day 3:

_____

_____

_____

Day 4:

_____

_____

_____

Day 5:

_____

_____

_____

Day 6:

_____

_____

_____

Day 7:

_____

_____

_____

Continuing writing down three good things each day even after you've finished this book.

THERAPISTS' TIPS

EXTRA TIDBITS

PROBLEM: YOU FIND YOURSELF PUSHING VERY HARD WITH THE WRITING TOOL

You definitely get credit for trying hard, but we don't want you to break the pencil lead or a sweat!

- Try taking more breaks and do the stretches. You may even need to set an alarm to force yourself to stop if you are a goal driven type of person.
- Try placing cardboard under the paper so that when you puncture through you know that you are pushing to hard. Try writing on tissue paper (the kind that you wrap gifts with) or on aluminum foil to force you to be more gentle.

WHY CURSIVE? WHY NOT PRINTING?

Even though this 3rd edition adds the illustration for printing, we encourage you to first learn cursive because cursive writing is easier to learn from a motor and a perceptual standpoint. Cursive writing causes less hand strain than printing. Learning cursive handwriting also diminishes the issues with needing to have even spaces that printing requires. We respect your right to choose your preferred style, so that's why our 3rd edition includes the upgrade! Thanks to those Handwriting Heroes who have gone before you and made this special request.

DOES WRITING HAVE TO BE LEGIBLE?

Each year, unreadable tax form addresses lead to $95,000,000 in tax refunds that do not reach the persons that should receive them.

According to the Writing Instrument Manufacturers Association, each year the U.S. loses over $200,000,000 for handwriting related reasons. This exceeds the losses due to computer hackers and computer related fraud.

Pharmacists report that they have difficulty reading 93% of the prescriptions that they receive.

No Pain, No Gain

While the research that demonstrates increased risk for someone who heavily uses one arm to have future overuse symptoms over time is scarce, those of us who work with persons with upper limb amputation know that many of our patients deal with pain in their non-amputated side or in their neck and back. Repetitive stress injuries refer to a group of diagnoses that include tendonitis and carpal tunnel syndrome. These diagnoses can result from other causes, but in this situation the person who heavily uses one upper limb may have problems with inflammation that results in tendonitis (inflammation of the tendon) or compression of a peripheral nerve (the cause of carpal tunnel syndrome). This can be caused by repetitive forceful grasping, pinching, or rotating, as well as prolonged static holding or awkward positioning. Repetitive tissue overloading leads to fatigue and fatigue leads to tissue failure and inflammation. Neck and back pain can result from poor posture and awkward positioning that is sometimes used to enable one to get the non-amputated arm into the area of the activity. We have included information on good posture and seating positions while practicing your handwriting to help you avoid these problems. We have also included information about stretching and rest breaks. These practices should be applied to the rest of your daily activities as well.

If you do have or develop any symptoms of pain or numbness in your arms or hands or pain in your neck or back you should seek medical attention early on. Many of these problems become more difficult to remediate the longer the person has had them. Treatment will often involve medical management of the anatomy that is involved as well as assessment of the activity; posture, environment, and tools that the person uses that may be contributing to the cause of the problem.

Week Five: Homework for Heroes

Day 1: Fill in the Personal Journal Entry on the corresponding page in this week's homework section.

Day 2: Go to the movie listings of your local newspaper. Copy the names of the films currently playing and the show times. This can be a practical exercise, so write it on paper if you want to refer to it later.

Day 3: Complete the coloring page in this week's homework section. HAVE FUN!!

Day 4: Complete the Dot-To-Dot figure.

Day 5: People often doodle while talking on the phone. If you only have one functioning hand, you may think this isn't possible. So here's your homework for today: call a friend, put the phone on speaker, then doodle as you converse. You can draw anything, write what they say, scribble back and forth ... just doodle!! HAVE FUN!!! Tell them what you're up to so they will visit for a while, and you'll get your doodle time in!

Day 6: Fill in the corresponding sheet in the homework.

Day 7: Fill in the corresponding sheet in the homework section.

Day One Homework

Complete the personal journal entry sheet below:

Today was great because _____

_____

Today I accomplished _____

_____

Today, the weather was _____

_____

Today's most stressful thing was _____

_____

_____

I spent today with _____

_____

_____

Tomorrow I plan to _____

_____

_____

One thing I couldn't stop thinking about today was _____

_____

_____

_____

Write the color key in below:

Day Six Homework

Use the guided sentences below to help you create a story of your childhood. If you'd rather, you can complete this on other paper and just write a story of your childhood.

I was born on _____ to

Mr. _____ and Mrs. _____.

I lived in _____.

My earliest memory of being young is _____

_____.

I went to Elementary school at _____

_____.

The names of some of my friends were _____

_____.

I can remember playing _____

_____.

I used to love to _____

_____.

Some things never change. I still enjoy _____

_____

_____.

My favorite grade in school was _____

because _____.

My most influential teacher was named _____.

Day Seven Homework

Use recall to answer these questions about your life and current living environment. If you can't remember, move your home/apartment/room to get the answers. Then write them below to complete all the sentences.

The type of soap in my shower is _____.

In my refrigerator, I have _____

_____

_____

_____.

I have (number) _____ pairs of shoes in my closet.

The sheets on my bed are (color/design) _____.

The laundry soap I use is _____.

The book I am reading now is called _____

and is written by _____.

The color of the walls in my bedroom are _____.

I could find a pen/pencil in my home if I looked in _____

_____.

Underneath my bathroom sink, I can find _____

_____

_____.

Extra Credit Week 5

Apple Dumplings

Copy the following recipe and send to a friend or family member.*

- 2 cans of Pillsbury® Croissant rolls
- 2 apples (Rome or Macintosh)
- 1 tsp cinnamon
- 1 cup of sugar
- 1 stick of butter
- 12 oz can of Mountain Dew

Melt butter and add the sugar. Mix. Set aside.
Peel and slice apples into eighths.
Place in a Ziploc baggie with the cinnamon and shake.
Remove apple pieces.
Wrap the apple in a Croissant roll.
Lay in an ungreased 9x13 glass-baking dish.
Cover the apple filled Croissant rolls with the butter/ sugar mixture.
Pour entire can of Mountain Dew into the baking dish.
Bake at 350 degrees F for 40-45 minutes.
Serve warm with ice cream.

*If you feel energetic (and hungry) make the recipe and share it with a friend.

WEEKLY COMPLIANCE SCORE_____

To see how much of the handwriting work you did this week, go back through the week and give yourself 1 point for each exercise you did and 1 point for each homework activity you did. If you did them ALL, you earned 91 compliance points. If you did the EXTRA CREDIT activity, you get NINE extra points, for a total score of 100!

Aim for at least 85 points each week.

LETTERS-PER-MINUTE SELF-ASSESSMENT:_____

Open a book you have at your home to any page (use the same book each week), set a timer or stopwatch for 5 minutes, and begin to copy the sentences from the book. After five minutes, STOP writing. Count each individual letter you wrote. Divide the total number by 5. This is your LETTERS-PER-MINUTE writing speed. You can now do two things: (1) Check out the Handwriting for Heroes website for a list of normative, grade-level values to see how fast you are writing, and (2) Use this number to set a personal goal of improvement for next week's writing speed.

Handwriting for Heroes

Week Six

It is important to set realistic goals for myself.
Be specific and think about improving your speed,
legibility, endurance, commitment and motivation.
This week my handwriting goal is:

_____

_____

_____

_____

Exercise 1: Warm-ups

Write the alphabet or *halph-a-bet* (i.e. only half of the alphabet) in each of the following boxes. Adjust the size of your script or printed letters to make the alphabet or *half-a-bet* fit.

Day 1:

Day 2:

Day 3:

Day 4:

Day 5:

Day 6:

Day 7:

Exercise 2: Train in the rain

Write two lines of the letter "r":

RRRRRR rrrrrrrrrrrr (R R R R r r r r r r)

Day 1:

Day 2:

Day 3:

Day 4:

Day 5:

Day 6:

Day 7:

Exercise 3: Range control

Trace the following curvy line pattern:

Day 1:

Day 2:

Day 3:

Day 4:

Day 5:

Day 6:

Day 7:

Exercise 4: Stretches

Copy the following two lines:

%%%%%%%%%%%%%%%%%%%%%%%%%%%%%

&&&&&&&&&&&&&&&&&&&&&&&&&&&&&&&

Day 1:

Day 2:

Day 3:

Day 4:

Day 5:

Day 6:

Day 7:

Exercise 5: Spit shine

Repetition and attention to detail put the polishing touches on anything. In the military, that's what makes a good "spit shine." Write two lines of these letters ach day:

pppppppppppppppppppp ddddddddddddddddd
PPPPPPPPPPPPPPPPPPPP ddddddddddddddddd

Day 1: _____

_____

Day 2: _____

_____

Day 3: _____

_____

Day 4: _____

_____

Day 5: _____

_____

Day 6: _____

_____

Day 7: _____

_____

Exercise 6: Speed drills

Much of our writing involves commonly used words. Copy two lines of these four small words. Work as fast as you can while maintaining the proper slant.

the the the of of of of on on on on are are are

the the the of of of of on on on on are are are

Day 1:

Day 2:

Day 3:

Day 4:

Day 5:

Day 6:

Day 7:

Exercise 7: Boot lacing

Cursive Learners: Keeping your pen on the paper, trace the letters in the sentence repeated below.
Print Learners: Below the cursive example:, write the sentence:

I have finished lots of writing exercises!

Day 1: *I have finished lots of writing exercises!*

Day 2: *I have finished lots of writing exercises!*

Day 3: *I have finished lots of writing exercises!*

Day 4: *I have finished lots of writing exercises!*

Exercise 7: Boot lacing (Continued)

Cursive Learners: Keeping your pen on the paper, trace the letters in the sentence repeated below.
Print Learners: Below the cursive example, write the sentence:

I have finished lots of writing exercises!

Day 5: *I have finished lots of writing exercises!*

Day 6: *I have finished lots of writing exercises!*

Day 7: *I have finished lots of writing exercises!*

Exercise 8: In cadence

Cursive Learners: Keeping your pen on the paper, trace the letters in the sentences below.
Print Learners: Below the cursive example, write the sentences:

I feel great about achieving my handwriting goals. I did it!

Day 1: *I feel great about achieving my handwriting goals. I did it!*

Day 2: *I feel great about achieving my handwriting goals. I did it!*

Day 3: *I feel great about achieving my handwriting goals. I did it!*

Day 4: *I feel great about achieving my handwriting goals. I did it!*

Exercise 8: In cadence (continued)

Cursive Learners: Trace the letters in the sentences below.
Print Learners: Below the cursive example, write the sentences:

I feel great about achieving my handwriting goals. I did it!

Day 5: *I feel great about achieving my handwriting goals. I did it!*

Day 6: *I feel great about achieving my handwriting goals. I did it!*

Day 7: *I feel great about achieving my handwriting goals. I did it!*

Exercise 9: Carbon copy

Ah yes, the following sentence contains every letter of the alphabet!

Don't question my mother named Zada K. Bigley who is exceptionally virtuous, fashionable, and joyful.

Don't question my mother named Zada K. Bigley who is exceptionally virtuous, fashionable, and joyful.

Day 1:

_____

_____

Day 2:

_____

_____

Day 3:

_____

_____

Day 4:

_____

_____

Day 5:

_____

_____

Day 6:

_____

_____

Day 7:

_____

_____

Exercise 10: Steady at the Ready

This exercise gives you daily practice combining straight line and loop letters. When you move between line and loop, strive to keep a consistent slant. Write the following sentence two times:

Never be too busy to meet someone new.

Never be too busy to meet someone new.

Day 1:

Day 2:

Day 3:

Day 4:

Day 5:

Day 6:

Day 7:

Exercise 11: Endurance training

Cursive Learners: Keep your lines of writing even across the page as you trace the following script.
Print Learners: Below the cursive example, write the sentence,

The days ahead are bright.

Day 1: *The days ahead are bright.*

Day 2: *The days ahead are bright.*

Day 3: *The days ahead are bright.*

Day 4: *The days ahead are bright.*

Day 5: *The days ahead are bright.*

Day 6: *The days ahead are bright.*

Day 7: *The days ahead are bright.*

Exercise 12: Esprit de corps

Copy the following sentence twice: *Exercise every day and maintain a positive attitude.*

Exercise every day and maintain a positive attitude.

*Review today's work and place a STAR next to today's best writing.

Day 1:

_____

_____

Day 2:

_____

_____

Day 3:

_____

_____

Day 4:

_____

_____

Day 5:

_____

_____

Day 6:

_____

_____

Day 7:

_____

_____

Exercise 13: Mighty Mindset Exercise: <u>Y</u>ou at Your Best

Your final positive psychology exercise is an opportunity for you show off both your handwriting skills and your personal strengths.

Write about a time when you feel that you were at your personal best. Make sure to include rich narrative details about what led up to this event, how you felt during it, what contributed to your success, and how you felt afterwards. Use the daily prompts from the homework assignment on the adjoining page for prompts.

_____

_____

_____

_____

_____

_____

_____

_____

_____

_____

_____

Review this story once every day this week and reflect on the personal strengths you have identified. Our brains cannot tell a significant difference between visualization and real experience. Therefore, by re-experiencing 'you at your best' you can continue to feel the effects of living that positive experience.

Exercise 13: Mighty Mindset Exercise: (Continued)

Day 1 thru 7: "Today I am going to demonstrate my personal best at…"

Day 1: _____

_____

Day 2: _____

_____

Day 3: _____

_____

Day 4: _____

_____

Day 5: _____

_____

Day 6: _____

_____

Day 7: _____

_____

Week Six: Homework for Heroes

Day 1: Write a story about something from your childhood. Share your wit and wisdom and how your childhood has influenced who you became. Mail it to your parents or to an influential teacher.

Day 2: Write every word you can think of that starts with the letter "S." See if you can come up with at least 100. When finished, check a dictionary to see the hundreds more "S" words in the English language.

Day 3: Complete the Coloring Page in this week's homework section.

Day 4: Complete the Dot-to-Dot figure in this week's homework section.

Day 5: Write the words to your favorite song. You may have to visit the Internet to find the complete lyrics (try www.LeosLyrics.com).

Day 6: Copy a paragraph that you've chosen from a magazine, book, or newspaper.

Day 7: Complete the sentence-completion exercise in this week's homework section.

Day Three Homework

Choose any colors to create contrasts between all the parts of the locomotive.

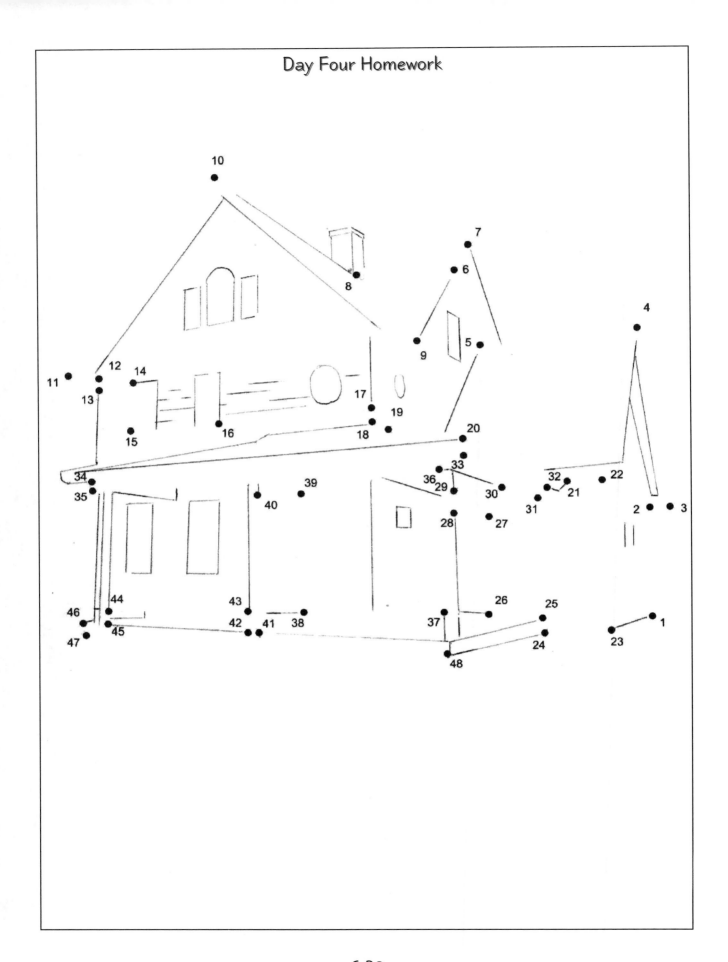

Day Seven Homework

Write (or print) the words that best express your thoughts to complete each statements.

1. Next month will be great because:

_____

_____

_____

2. I feel like I have made progress toward the following life goals:

_____

_____

_____

3. This is how people usually describe me:

_____

_____

_____

4. This is why going to _____ was the most exciting vacation I ever took:

_____

_____

_____

5. If I had a million dollars, I would

_____

_____

_____

Self-Perception Questionnaire on Handwriting Ability Post-Test

Instructions: Using a 0 - 10 Scale, please answer the following questions about your handwriting ability.

1. How does your handwriting ability *today* compare to your handwriting ability *before* your limb injury in terms of **readability**?
Readability means that someone who doesn't know you can read what you wrote.

0	1	2	3	4	5	6	7	8	9	10
not at all alike										exactly alike

2. How does your handwriting ability *today* compare to your handwriting ability *before* your limb injury in terms of **speed**?
Speed means the pace at which you are writing.

0	1	2	3	4	5	6	7	8	9	10
not at all alike										exactly alike

3. How does your handwriting ability *today* compare to your handwriting *before* your limb injury in terms of **appearance.**
Appearance means the shape, size, slant, and style of your writing.

0	1	2	3	4	5	6	7	8	9	10
not at all alike										exactly alike

4. How **confident** are you in your writing ability?
Confidence means that you are sure of your ability to write.

0	1	2	3	4	5	6	7	8	9	10
not confident at all										exactly alike

5. How **important** is learning to write again?
Important means that you value spending your time learning to write again.

0	1	2	3	4	5	6	7	8	9	10
not confident at all										exactly alike

Extra Credit Week 6

Remember in 5ᵗʰ grade English class when the teacher taught you what the word "onomatopoeia" meant? Let us refresh your memories. *Onomatopoeia* means the formation or use of a word that can imitate a sound associated with the action that it refers to. For example: "buzz" or "bang!"

List as many onomatopoetic words as you can think of!

You can <u>definitely</u> think of ten!!!

1. _____

2. _____

3. _____

4. _____

5. _____

6. _____

7. _____

8. _____

9. _____

10. _____

WEEKLY COMPLIANCE SCORE_____

To see how much of the handwriting work you did this week, go back through the week and give yourself 1 point for each exercise you did and 1 point for each homework activity you did. If you did them ALL, you earned 91 compliance points. If you did the EXTRA CREDIT activity, you get NINE extra points, for a total score of 100!

Aim for at least 85 points each week.

LETTERS-PER-MINUTE SELF-ASSESSMENT:_____

Open a book you have at your home to any page (use the same book each week), set a timer or stopwatch for 5 minutes, and begin to copy the sentences from the book. After five minutes, STOP writing. Count each individual letter you wrote. Divide the total number by 5. This is your LETTERS-PER-MINUTE writing speed. You can now do two things: (1) Check out the Handwriting for Heroes website for a list of normative, grade-level values to see how fast you are writing, and (2) Use this number to set a personal goal of improvement for next week's writing speed.

Certificate of Completion

This certificate is awarded to

in recognition of valuable contributions

Signature _____ Date _____

Signature _____ Date _____

ABOUT THE AUTHORS

Katie Yancosek is an officer in the Army Medical Specialist Corps. She graduated from Gannon University with a Bachelor's of Science degree in occupational therapy, from Eastern Kentucky University with a Master's of Science degree in occupational therapy, and from the University of Kentucky with a PhD in rehabilitation sciences. She currently lives in San Antonio with her husband and two sons.

Kristin Gulick has been enjoying her practice as an occupational therapist for more than 25 years. She graduated from University of Puget Sound and began her practice working with children at Shriner's Hospital in Portland, OR. Kristin's career path led her to focus on rehabilitation of the upper extremity and she became a certified hand therapist in 1996. In the past, Kristin served as the Director of Therapy Services at Advanced Arm Dynamics, where she enjoyed working with clients with upper limb loss in their rehabilitation process. Currently, Kristin lives in Bend, OR where she is the owner/director of Hand and Arm Therapy of Central Oregon.

Amanda Sammons is an officer in the Army Medical Specialist Corps. She graduated from West Virginia University with a Bachelor's of Science degree in athletic training, from Shenandoah University with a Master's of Science degree in occupational therapy, and from Baylor University with a Doctor of Science degree in occupational therapy. She currently lives in San Antonio, Texas with her husband.

Erin Spears drew the dot-to-dots and coloring pages for this manual. He works in Maryland where he lives with his wife and two children. His love of art began as a child and his favorite medium is graphite. His latest work is illustrating children's books.

BIBLIOGRAPHY

Alston, J. (1983). A legibility index: Can handwriting be measured? *Education Review, 35*, 237-242.

Achor, S. (2012, January). Positive intelligence. *Harvard Business Review*, 2-4.

Andree, M. E., & Maitra, K. K. (2002). Intermanual transfer of a new writing occupation in young adults without disability. *Occupational Therapy International, 9*(1), 41-56.

Annett, M. (1985). *Left, right, hand and brain: the right shift theory.* London: Erlbaum.

Backman, C., Cork, S., Gibson, G., & Parsons, J. (1992). Assessment of hand function: the relationship between pegboard dexterity and applied dexterity. *Canadian Journal of Occupational Therapy, 59*, 208-213.

Bass-Haugen, J., Mathiowetz, V., & Flinn, N. (2007). Optimizing motor behavior using the occupational therapy task-oriented approach. In M. Vining-Radomski & C. A. Trombly-Latham (Eds.), *Occupational therapy for physical dysfunction* (6th ed., pp. 599-617). Philadelphia: Lippincott Williams & Wilkins.

Beaule, P. E., Dervin, G. F., Giachino, A. A., Rody, K., Grabowski, J., & Fazekas, A. (2000). Self-reported disability following distal radius fractures: The influence of hand dominance. *Journal of Hand Surgery, 25*(3), 476-482.

Berninger, V. W. (1994). *Reading and writing acquisition: A developmental neuropsychological perspective.* Dubuque, IA: Brown & Benchmark.

Bicchi, A. (2000). Hands for dextrous manipulation and robust grasping: A difficult road toward simplicity. *Transaction of Robotics and Automation, 16*(6), 652-662.

Bonney, M. A. (1992). Understanding and assessing handwriting difficulty: Perspectives from the literature. *Australian Occupational Therapy Journal, 39*(3), 7-15.

Boyes, A. (2013, February 12). 6 Mindfulness Exercises That Each Take Less Than 1 Minute. Retrieved August 25, 2014.

Burr, V. (2002). Judging gender from samples of adult handwriting: Accuracy and use of cues. *Journal of Social Psychology, 142*(6), 691-700.

Chan, S. W., & LaStayo, P. (2003). Hand therapy management following mutilating hand injuries. *Hand Clinics, 19*, 133-148.

Chieh, L., Wenbin, Z., & Nuttall, R. L. (2003). Familial handedness and spatial ability: A study with Chinese students aged 14-24. *Brain Cognition, 51*, 375-384.

Christensen, C. A. (2005). The role of orthographic-motor integration in the production of creative and well-structured written text for students in secondary school. *Educational Psychology, 25*(5), 441.

Chu, S. (1997). Occupational therapy for children with handwriting difficulties: A framework for evaluation and treatment. *British Journal of Occcupational Therapy, 60*, 514-520.

Connelly, V., Dockrell, J. E., & Barnett, J. (2005). The slow handwriting of undergraduate students constrains overall performance in exam essays. *Educational Psychology, 25*(1), 99.

Connelly, V., Gee, D., & Walsh, E. (2007). A comparison of keyboarded and handwritten compositions and the relationship with transcription speed. *British Journal of Educational Psychology, 77*(2), 479-492.

Cornhill, H., & Case-Smith, J. (1996). Factors that relate to good and poor handwriting. *American Journal of Occupational Therapy, 50*, 732-739.

Dixon, R. A., Kurzman, D., & Friesen, I. C. (1993). Handwriting performance in younger and older adults: age, familiarity, and practice effects. *Psychology and Aging, 8*(3), 360-370.

Doak, C. C., Doak, L. G., & Root, J. H. (1996). *Teaching patients with low literacy skills* (2nd ed.). Philadelphia: J.B. Lippincott.

Doyen, A. L., & Carlier, M. (2002). Measuring handedness: A validation study of Bishop's reaching card test. *Laterality, 7*(2), 115-130.

Dunsmuir, S., & Blatchford, P. (2004). Predictors of writing competence in 4- to 7-year old children. *British Journal of Educational Psychology, 74*(3), 461.

Elbert, T., & Rockstroh, B. (2004). Reorganization of human cerebral cortex: the range of changes following use and injury. *The Neuroscientist, 10*(2), 129-141.

Escalante-Mead, R. R., Minshew, N. J., & Sweeney, J. A. (2003). Abnormal brain lateralization in high-functioning autism. *Journal of Autism and Developmental Disorders, 33*(5), 539-539.

Faddy, K., McCluskey, A., & Lannin, N. A. (2008). Interrater reliability of a new Handwriting Assessment Battery for adults. *American Journal of Occupational Therapy, 62*, 595-599.

Feder, K. P., & Majnemer, A. (2007). Handwriting development, competency, and intervention. *Developmental Medicine and Child Neurology, 49*(4), 312-317.

Ferrari, M. (2007). Cognitive performance and left-handedness: comparative analyses in adults with seizures, physical, psychological and learning disorders in a rehabilitation setting. *Journal of Rehabilitation, 73*(1), 47-54.

Flower, L., & Hayes, J. R. (1980). The dynamics of composing: Making plans and juggling constraints. In L. W. Gregg & E. R. Steinberg (Eds.), *Cognitive processes in writing* (pp. 31-50). Hillsdale, NJ: Lawrence Erlbaum Associates, Inc.

Fontana, P., Dagnino, F., Cocito, L., & Balestrino, M. (2008). Handwriting as a gauge of cognitive status: a novel forensic tool for posthumous evaluation of testamentary capacity. *Neurological Sciences, 29*(4), 257-261.

Gander, F., Proyer, R.T., Ruch, W., & Wyss, T. (2013). Strength-based positive interventions: Further evidence for their potential in enhancing well-being and alleviating depression. Journal of Happiness Studies, 14, 1241-1259.

Goez, H., & Zelnick, N. (2008). Handedness in patients with developmental coordination disorder. *Journal of Child Neurology, 23*(2), 151-154.

Graham, S. (1992). Issues in handwriting instruction. *Focus on Exceptional Children, 25*, 1-14.

Graham, S., Berninger, V. W., Weintraub, N., & Schafer, W. (1998). Development of handwriting speed and legibility in grades 1-9. *Journal of Educational Research, 92*(42-56).

Graham, S., & Harris, K. R. (2005). Improving the writing performance of young struggling writers: Theoretical and programmatic research from the center on accelerating student learning. *The Journal of Special Education, 39*(1), 19-33.

Graham, S., Weintraub, N., & Berninger, V. W. (1998). The relationship between handwriting style and speed and legibility. *Journal of Educational Research, 91*(5), 290.

Granville, D., Ehrman, L., & Perelle, I. B. (1980). Laterality survey: questionnaire results. *Mensa Bulletin, 239*, 26.

Henderson, S., Sen, R., & Brown, B. (1989). Writing quickly- Do we teach it? and if so how? A pilot study. *Handwriting Review*, 46-50.

Jones, D., & Christensen, C. A. (1999). Relationship between automaticity in handwriting and students' ability to generate written text. *Journal of Educational Psychology, 91*, 44-49.

Jongmans, M. J., Linthorst-Bakker, E., Westenberg, Y., & Smits-Engelsman, B. C. M. (2003). Use of a task-oriented self-instruction method to support children in primary school with poor handwriting quality and speed. *Human Movement Science, 22*(4), 549-566.

Josse, G., & Tzourio-Mazoyer, N. T. (2004). Hemisphere specialization for language. *Brain Research Rev, 44*, 1-12.

Kelso, J. A., & Fuchs, A. (1995). Self-organizing dynamics of the human brain: Critical instabilities and Sil'nikov chaos. *Chaos, 5*(1), 64-69.

Kerner, E. A., & Fitzpatrick, M. R. (2007). Integrating writing into psychotherapy practice: A matrix of change processes and structural dimensions. *Psychotherapy: Theory, Research, Practice, Training, 44*(3), 333-346.

Kielhofner, G. (1995). *A model of human occupation: Theory and application.* Baltimore: Williams & Wilkins.

Kimmerle, M., Mainwaring, L., & Borenstein, M. (2003). The functional repertoire of the hand and its application to assessment. *American Journal of Occupational Therapy, 57*(5), 489-498.

Kleim, J. A., Barbay, S., Cooper, N. R., Hogg, T. M., Reidel, C. N., Remple, M. S., et al. (2002). Motor learning-dependent synaptogenesis is localized to functionally reorganized motor cortex. *Neurobiology of learning and memory, 77*(1), 63-77.

Kleim, J. A., & Jones, T. A. (2008). Principles of experience-dependent neural plasticity: implications for rehabilitation after brain damage. *Journal of Speech, Language, and Hearing Research, 51*(1), S225-239.

Kloppel, S., Vongerichten, A., Van Eimeren, T., Frackowiak, R. S. J., & Siebner, H. R. (2007). Can left-handedness be switched? Insights from an early switch of handwriting.

Kutner, M., Greenberg, E., & Baer, J. (2005). A first look at the literacy of America's adults in the 21st century. Retrieved January 15, 2010, from http://nces.ed.gov/NAAL/PDF/2006470.PDF

Latash, L. P., & Latash, M. L. (1994). A new book by N. A. Bernstein: "On dexterity and its development". *Journal of Motor Behavior, 26*(1), 56-62.

Laufer, L. (1995). *Callirobics. Handwriting skills for adults.* Charlottesville, VA: Callirobics.

Law, M., Cooper, B. A., Strong, S., Stewart, D., Rigby, P., & Letts, L. (1996). The Person-Environment-Occupational Model: a transactive approach to occupational performance. *Canadian Journal of Occupational Therapy, 63* (1), 9-23.

Lewison, T. S., & Zubin, J. (1942). *Handwriting analysis.* New York: King's Crown Press.

Lubrano, V., Roux, F. E., & Demonet, J. F. (2004). Writing-specific sites in frontal areas: a cortical stimulation study. *Journal of Neurosurgery, 101*(5), 787-798.

Martin, H. J. (1994). *The History and Power of Writing.* Chicago: The University of Chicago Press.

Mayer, A. R., & Kosson, D. S. (2000). Handedness and psychopathy. *Neuropsychiatry, Neuropsychology & Behavioral Neurology, 13*(4), 233-238.

McMahon, R., McCluskey, A., & Lannin, N. A. (2008). Examining handwriting and communication technology use by Australian adults aged between 18 and 54 years. *Journal of Psychology and Aging, In review.*

McManus, C. (2002). *Right hand left hand: The origins of asymmetry in brains, bodies, atoms and cultures.* Cambridge, MA: Harvard University Press.

McManus, I. C., Bryden, M. P., & Johnson, M. H. (1993). The neurobiology of handedness, language, and cerebral dominance: A model for the molecular genetics of behavior. In *Brain development and cognition: A reader.* (pp. 679-702). Malden, MA US: Blackwell Publishing.

Muenzen, P., Kasch, M., Greenberg, S., Fullennwrider, L., Taylor, P., & Dimick, M. (2002). A new practice analysis of hand therapy. *Journal of Hand Therapy, 3,* 215-225.

Niemiec, R.M. (2013) OK now what? Taking action with strength. Retrieved August 15, 2014 from http://www.viacharacter.org/resources/ok-now-what-taking-action-with-strength-by-ryan-m-niemiec-psy-d/

Nudo, R. J., Milliken, G. W., Jenkins, W. M., & Merzenich, M. M. (1996). Use-dependent alterations of movement representations in primary motor cortex of adult squirrel monkeys. *Journal of Neuroscience, 16*(2), 785-807.

Nudo, R. J., Wise, B. M., SiFuentes, F., & Milliken, G. W. (1996). Neural substrates for the effects of rehabilitative training on motor recovery after ischemic infarct. *Science, 272*(5269), 1791-1794.

Oldfield, R. C. (1971). The assessment and analysis of handedness: the Edinburgh Handedness Inventory. *Neuropsychologia, 9,* 97-113.

Parush, S., Levanon-Erez, N., & Weintraub, N. (1998). Ergonomic factors influencing handwriting performance. *Work, 11*(3), 295-305.

Parush, S., Pindak, V., Hanh-Markowitz, J., & Mazor-Karsenty, T. (1998). Does fatigue influence children's handwriting performance? *Work, 11*(3), 307-313.

Pennebaker, J. W., & Seagal, J. D. (1999). Forming a story: The health benefits of narrative. Journal of Clinical Psychology, 55, 1243-1254.

Peterson, C., & Seligman, M. (2004). Character strengths and virtues: A handbook and classification. USA: Oxford University Press.

Peverly, S. T. (2006). The importance of handwriting speed in adult writing. *Developmental Neuropsychology, 29*(1), 197-216.

Plaskins-Thornton, T. (1996). *Handwriting in America.* New Haven, CT: Yale University Press.

Price, S. (2011). Positive psychology worksheet: Three good things exercise. Retrieved August 15, 2014, from http://positiveintelligence.com.au /doc/Positive_psychology__3GT_Worksheet.pdf

Rajan, P., Premkumar, R., Rajkumar, P., & Richard, J. (2005). The impact of hand dominance and ulnar and median nerve impairment on strength and basic daily activities. *Journal of Hand Therapy, 18*, 40-45.

Rose, D. J. (1997). *A Multilevel Approach to the Study of Motor Control and Learning.* Needham Heights: Allyn & Bacon.

Rosenblum, S., Goldstand, S., & Parush, S. (2006). Relationships among biomechanical ergonomic factors, handwriting product quality, handwriting efficiency, and computerized handwriting process measures in children with and without handwriting difficulties. *American Journal of Occupational Therapy, 60*(1), 28-39.

Rosenblum, S., & Werner, P. (2006). Assessing the handwriting process in healthy elderly persons using a computerized system. *Aging Clinical Experimental Research, 18*(5), 433-439.

Sasaki, K. T., & Gemba, H. (1987). Plasticity of cortical function related to voluntary movement motor learning and compensation following brain dysfunction. *Acta Neurochirurgica, 41(supplement)*, 18-28.

Satz, P., Orsini, D. L., Saslow, E., & Henry, R. (1985). The pathological left-handedness syndrome. *Brain and Cognition, 4*(1), 27-46.

Schmidt, R. A., & Wrisberg, C. A. (2000). *Motor learning and performance.* Champaign, IL: Human Kinetics.

Schmidt, R. A., & Wrisberg, C. A. (2008). *Motor learning and performance: A situation-based learning approach* (4 ed.). Champaign, IL: Human Kinetics.

Schneck, C. M. (1991). Comparison of pencil-grip patterns in first graders with good and poor writing skills. *American Journal of Occupational Therapy, 45*(8), 701-706.

Schoneveld, K., Wittink, H., & Takken, R. (2009). Clinemetric evaluation of measurement tools used in hand therapy to assess activity and participation. *Journal of Hand Therapy, 22*, 221-236.

Shea, J. B., & Zimny, S. T. (1983). Context effects in memory and learning movement information. In R. A. Magill (Ed.), *Memory and control of action* (pp. 345-366). Amsterdam: North-Holland.

Seligman, M.E., Steen, T., Park, N., & Peterson, C. (2005). Positive psychology progress: Empirical validation of interventions. American Psychologist, 60(4), 410-421.

Seligman, M. (2011, April). Recovering from failure: Building resilience. Harvard Business Review, 101-106.

Seligman, M.E., Ernst, R.M., Gillham, J., Reivich, K., & Linkins, M. (2009). Positive education: Positive psychology and classroom interventions. Oxford Review of Education, 35(3), 293-311.

Shen, I. h., Kang, S.-m., & Wu, C.-y. (2003). Comparing the effect of different design of desks with regard to motor accuracy in writing performance of students with cerebral palsy. *Applied Ergonomics, 34*(2), 141-147.

Shiri, R., Varonen, H., Helivaara, M., & Viikari-Juntura, E. (2007). Hand dominance in upper extremity musculoskeletal disorders. *Journal of Rheumatology, 34*(5), 1076-1082.

Siebner, H. R., Limmer, C., Peinemann, A., Drzezga, A., Bloem, B. R., Schwaiger, M., et al. (2002). Long-term consequences of switching handedness: a positron emission tomography study on handwriting in "converted" lefthanders. *Journal of Neuroscience, 22*(7), 2816-2825.

Smits-Engelsman, B. C. M., & van Galen, G. P. (1997). Dysgraphia in children: Lasting psychomotor deficiency or transient developmental delay? *Journal of Experimental Child Psychology, 67*(164-184.).

Sovik, N., Arntzen, O., & Karlsdottir, R. (1993). Relations between writing speed and some other parameters in handwriting. *Journal of Human Movement Studies, 25*, 133-150.

Ste-Marie, D. M., Clark, S. E., Findlay, L. C., & Latimer, A. E. (2004). High levels of contextual interference enhance handwriting skill acquisition. *Journal of Motor Behavior, 36*(1), 115-126.

Steele-Johnson, D. (2000). Goal orientation and task demand effects on motivation, affect, and performance. *The Journal of Applied Psychology, 85*(5), 724-728.

Stratford, P. W., Binkley, J. M., & Stratford, D. (2001). Development and initial validation of the Upper Extremity Functional Index. *Physiotherapy Canada, 52*, 259-267, 281.

Suen, C. (1983). Handwriting generation, perception, and recognition. *Acta Psychologica, 54*, 295-312.

Sveller, C., Briellmann, R. S., Saling, M. M., Lillywhite, L., Abbott, D. F., Masterton, R. A., et al. (2006). Relationship between language lateralization and handedness in left-hemispheric partial epilepsy. *Neurology, 67*(10), 1813-1817.

Teixeira, L. A., & Okazaki, V. H. A. (2007). Shift of manual preference by lateralized practice generalizes to related motor tasks. *Experimental Brain Research, 183*, 417-423.

Teulings, H. L., & Schomaker, L. R. B. (1993). Invarient properties between stroke features in handwriting. *Acta Psychologica, 82*, 69-88.

Toepfer, S.M., & Walker, K. (2009). Letters of gratitude: Improving well-being through expressive writing. Journal of Writing Research, 1(3), 181-198.

Toepfer, S.M., Cichy, K., & Peters, P. (2012). Letters of gratitude: Further evidence for author benefits. Journal of Happiness Studies, 13, 187-201.

Tomcheck, S. D., & Schneck, C. M. (2006). Evaluation of handwriting. In A. Henderson & C. Pehoski (Eds.), *Hand function in the child: Foundations for remediation* (pp. 291-318). St. Louis: Mosby.

Tucha, O., Tucha, L., & Lange, K. W. (2008). Graphonomics, automaticity and handwriting assessment. *Literacy, 42* (3), 145-155.

van Galen, G. (1991). Handwriting: Issues for a psychomotor theory. *Human Movement Science, 10*(165-191).

van Gemmert, A. W. A., & Teulings, H.-L. (2006). Advances in graphonomics: Studies on fine motor control, its development and disorders. *Human Movement Science, 25*(4-5), 447-453.

Wada, J. A., Clarke, R. J., & Hamm, A. E. (1975). Cerebral hemispheric assymmetry in humans. *Archives of Neurology, 32*, 239-246.

Walker, L., & Henneberg, M. (2007). Writing with the non-dominant hand: cross-handedness trainability in adult individuals. *Laterality, 12*(2), 121-130.

Walsh, W. W., Belding, N. N., Taylor, E., & Nunley, J. A. (1993). The effect of upper extremity trauma on handedness. *American Journal of Occupational Therapy, 47*(9), 787-795.

Weintraub, N., & Graham, S. (1998). Writing legibly and quickly: A study of children's ability to adjust their handwriting to meet common classroom demands. *Learning Disabilities Research and Practice, 13*, 146-152.

Weintraub, N., & Graham, S. (2000). The contribution of gender, orthographic, finger function, and visual-motor processes to the prediction of handwriting status. *Occupational therapy Journal of Research, 20*(2), 121-140.

Woodward, S., & Swinth, Y. (2002). Multisensory approach to handwriting remediation: Perceptions of school-based occupational therapists. *American Journal of Occupational Therapy, 56*(3), 305-312.

Zellermayer, M., & Margolin, I. (2005). Teacher educators' professional learning described through the lens of complexity theory. *Teachers College Record, 107*, 1275-1304.

Ziviani, J., & Watson-Will, A. (1998). Writing speed and legibility of 7-14 year old school students using modern cursive script. *Australian Occupational Therapy Journal, 45*, 59-64

REORDER FORM

Therapists get FREE SHIPPING in the USA*
and save big when they buy direct from the publisher!

Name_____

Organization_____

Address_____

_____

City_____State_____Zip_____

Country_____

Please send me *Handwriting for Heroes* _____ copies @ $21.00 = $_____

Please upgrade to Priority Mail for $2 extra PER COPY = $_____
standard shipping is USPS MediaMail—allow 2-4 weeks
Outside USA please add $6 per copy for postage   **Total** _$_____

I enclose payment by:

[ ] Check or Money-order   [ ] VISA [ ] MasterCard [ ] Amex [ ] Discover

Card Number _____ Expires _____

CVV code (3-digits on signature strip)_____

Authorized signature (for credit card orders)_____

Email address (order confirmation only) _____

FAX this page to 734-663-6861 or return by mail

Loving Healing Press, Inc.
5145 Pontiac Trail
Ann Arbor, MI 48105-9627

*Free shipping includes 50 states & APO/FPO addresses

www.LovingHealing.com

Loving Healing Press

ADDRESSING THE EMOTIONAL SIDE OF HEALING

Coping With
Physical Loss and Disability

A Workbook by Rick Ritter, MSW

This workbook provides more than 50 questions and exercises designed to empower those with physical loss and disability to better understand and accept their ongoing processes of loss and recovery. These exercises were distilled from ten years of clinical social work experience with clients suffering from quadriplegia, paraplegia, amputation(s), cancer, severe burns, hepatitis, lupus, HIV/AIDs, and neuromuscular disorders.

Exercises engage the emotional, physical, mental, and spiritual aspects of the client to increase ability and acceptance in critical areas of functioning including self-care, support systems, coping skills, scheduling their life, identity, and dealing with past vs. future, feelings, beliefs, and identifying positive outcomes.

"This workbook provides very good stimulus for focusing on issues that are crucial for better coping with loss and disability."

—Beni R. Jakob, PhD,
Israeli Arthritis Foundation (INBAR)

"This workbook is a tremendous resource that is practical and easy to use. The author shows his connection with this material in a way from which we can all benefit."

—Geneva Reynaga-Abiko, Psy.D., Clinical Psychologist
University of Illinois, Urbana-Champaign Counseling Center

About the Author

Rick Ritter, MSW, a veteran with disabilities and a social worker, has worked with hundreds of clients who have experienced extreme physical loss and disability. This workbook is a distillation of the very best questions and exercises to draw the client towards re-taking control of their life. He has competed in international events for disabled athletes. Ritter was also a major contributor to *got parts? An Insider's Guide to Managing Life Successfully with Dissociative Identity Disorder*. He currently resides in Fort Wayne, Indiana.

List: $17.95 * ISBN 1-932690-18-2 * eBook Editions Available
More info at www.PhysicalLoss.com